No-Glamour® Memory

by Constance Lund Rozendaal and Carolyn P. Snyder

Skills	**Ages**
■ auditory memory	■ 5 through 18
■ visual memory	**Grades**
■ language	■ kindergarten through 12

Evidence-Based Practice

According to the Preferred Practice Patterns for the Profession of Speech-Language Pathology (2004, http://www.asha.org/members/deskref-journals/deskref/default) and the Clinical Guidelines of the Royal College of Speech & Language Therapists (www.rcslt.org/resources, 2005), and *A Mind at a Time* by Dr. Mel Levine (2002), the following therapy principles are supported:

■ Intervention should address processing of varied types of information and in the context of varied activities and settings (e.g., ability to attend to, perceive, organize, and remember verbal and nonverbal information including social cues, reasoning, and problem solving).

■ Therapy should include memory strategies to support and organize learning, such as recoding, paraphrasing, chunking, forming associations, writing down steps, and/or creating pictures in the mind.

■ Children need to be systematic in their use of memory by developing learning plans for remembering information, especially before tests.

■ Students should master the tricks of remembering something and include them in their learning plans. The best way to remember something is to change it (e.g., if it's visual, make it verbal; if it's verbal, create a diagram).

■ Recall and recognition work best when used often. Memory strategies and learning plans need to be practiced and exercised regularly.

This book incorporates the above principles and is based on expert professional practice.

LinguiSystems®

LinguiSystems, Inc.
3100 4th Avenue
East Moline, IL 61244

FAX: 800-577-4555
Phone: 800-776-4332
E-mail: service@linguisystems.com
Web: linguisystems.com

Printed in the U.S.A.

ISBN 978-0-7606-0743-5

About the Authors

Constance Lund Rozendaal, M.S., CCC-SLP, is currently in private practice in the Seattle/Bellevue area focusing on language and learning. In addition to the clinic setting, Constance has worked in public and private schools and in homes. She received her B.S. in Speech and Hearing Sciences from the University of Washington and her M.S. in Communicative Disorders from the University of Wisconsin-Madison. Constance lives in Issaquah, Washington with her husband.

Carolyn P. Snyder, M.S. CCC-SLP, is currently in private practice. Her clinical experiences range from public to private schools and from clinic to home settings. Carolyn received her B.S. and M.S. in Communicative Disorders from the University of Wisconsin-Madison. Carolyn resides in San Francisco with her husband and daughter.

Prior to opening their private practices, Constance and Carolyn spent five years together running a language and learning clinic in the San Francisco Bay Area.

Acknowledgments

We would like to thank the students, parents, and professionals who work with us. A special thank you to Natalie Varney, Carolyn Compton, and Pat Morrissey who have been influential in our professional lives. Additionally, we would like to thank our husbands and families.

Edited by Lauri Whiskeyman
Cover Design by Jason Platt
Page Layout by Lisa Parker
Illustrations on page 69 by Danny Whiskeyman, Age 9

Table of Contents

Introduction

Memory is a critical component for academic success. Researchers have hypothesized that students diagnosed with language-based learning disabilities possess intact structures in the brain but do not have adequate language processing abilities. These students neglect to activate working memory spontaneously as well as fail to integrate new information into existing memory files (Lanter 2005).

Often memory is viewed as two separate storage mechanisms within the brain that differ in several ways. However, some research indicates that they are not actually different mechanisms but different manifestations of the same mechanism, such as different levels of processing. For the purpose of this book, we will hold to the belief that memory is generally divided into long- and short-term memory (Higbee 2001).

Memory can be thought of as a filing cabinet. Short-term memory is the small basket on the top of the cabinet that holds all new files, or where newly-acquired information goes. This new information is registered by the sensory organs and hippocampus, a structure in the brain. New information must pass through this basket before being filed into the larger spaces within the cabinet. This basket holds only limited information, such as an unfamiliar phone number or the information given in a news story. If this information is not relevant, such as all the details of a newscast, the information will be released and forgotten. If it is relevant to the listener, it will be retained in the filing cabinet of the long-term memory (Fotuhi 2004).

Long-term memory is the space within the filing cabinet where information is stored for retrieval. This storage facility is located in the cortex of the brain. Within this "cabinet," information can be filed like books in a library. If information is poorly filed, or organized, it can be hard to pull up (remember) later. Information must be coded and categorized for efficient transfer and recall. Information stored here can range from material learned for an upcoming test to memories from a graduation or wedding (Fotuhi 2004).

Dr. Mel Levine, professor of Pediatrics and Director of the Clinical Center for the Study of Development and Learning at the University of North Carolina, Chapel Hill, believes that memory is an important part of many different academic tasks. Information must be taken in and integrated with what is already known in order to perform the tasks. Combining new information with previously-stored information and skills is at the center of learning. Dr. Levine's model for memory includes short-term, long-term, and the link between the two – active working memory (Levine 2002).

1. *Short-term memory*: This is the part of the memory system that allows for brief retention of new information (typically two seconds).

Deficits in this memory system may include the following:
- inability to chunk information
- inability to register information quickly enough
- failure to make attention and memory work together

Suggestions for remediation of short-term memory difficulties include whispering information under your breath, forming pictures in your mind, putting visuals into words, and paraphrasing information.

2. *Active working memory*: This part of the memory system links short- and long-term memory together. It involves the information you hold in your mind at the time you attempt to complete a task (i.e., not as brief as short-term memory nor as permanent as long-term memory).

Deficits in this memory system may include the following:
- failure to remember information just read
- inability to hold onto parts of a task or activity long enough to act on it or complete it
- inability to bind different parts of memory together (i.e., a student forgets the question while trying to come up with an answer)

Suggestions for remediation of active working memory difficulties include underlining main points while reading and reviewing them at the end of each page and identifying key ideas.

3. *Long-term memory*: This part of the memory system acts as the warehouse for preserving knowledge, skills, and life experiences.

Deficits in this memory system may include the following:
- inability to file information as pairs (e.g., names with faces, countries with capitals)
- difficulty following procedures (e.g., science experiments, math computations)
- difficulty categorizing information
- inability to remember rules or patterns (e.g., letter-sound correspondence)

Suggestions for remediation of long-term memory difficulties include linking; rehearsing; writing information down; drawing diagrams, charts, or graphs; and repeated exposure to memory tasks.

Through our work in clinic and school settings, we have found limited resources that focus on helping students improve memory skills. Many clinical materials that target memory, such as textbooks or workbooks, are written in narrative formats and require too much time to filter out relevant date or to create activities for students. We wanted straightforward, flexible

6

materials that taught alternative approaches to learning and relied on multiple kinds of input (e.g., visual, auditory, kinesthetic). We also wanted materials that were fun for students. When we couldn't find what we were looking for, we created *No-Glamour Memory*.

No-Glamour Memory is for students ages 5–18 who struggle to recall, retain, or process either auditory or visual information. We avoided the monotony and often ineffectiveness of drill and practice with a variety of fun, functional activities using classroom-relevant topics (e.g., social studies, language arts, science). We used a multi-modality approach to help meet the needs of students with a variety of learning styles. *No-Glamour Memory* was also created with parents in mind, offering strategies and exercises that can be done at home. All of the activities require minimal preparation and generalize to classroom work.

No-Glamour Memory is divided into two main sections, *Auditory Memory* and *Visual Memory*. At the beginning of each section, you will find a pretest/posttest. Have each student complete the test before doing the exercises in the section. If a student achieves 80%, it is considered passing. This indicates that the student has a strong understanding and use of the strategies that focus on improving memory of information that is heard, written, or seen.

If a student scores below the 80th percentile, identify which strategy or strategies the student is having difficulty with and begin therapy there. Then when the student has completed the exercises, have him take the test again. Compare the results to the original score. Continue remediation as needed.

Because there are many reasons a child may perform poorly on an item on the pretest, poor performance should not be interpreted as being evidence of a particular impairment and should not be used to make a particular diagnosis. The child's performance should only be used to guide your clinical judgment as it pertains to the formulation of an appropriate therapy program, needed accommodations, or further assessment.

Each unit within *Auditory Memory* and *Visual Memory* contains 10 exercises (except Saying, Tracing, Writing, & Drawing Sounds on pages 183-188). The exercises, as well as the items within each exercise, are arranged in order from easier to more difficult items. Choose appropriate exercises depending on your student's abilities.

The book also includes student and parent handouts:

- *Enhancing Memory Skills* — ways to enhance memory skills
- *Checking Up: Which Strategy Works Best for You?* — a rating scale for students to complete to help determine which memory strategy(ies) works best for them
- *Strategies for Auditory Memory* and *Strategies for Visual Memory* — lists of auditory and visual memory strategies and their corresponding goals

7

The *Auditory Memory* section has eight strategies that focus on improving memory of information that is heard. These activities are intended to be completed orally.

- Rehearsing & Subvocalizing
- Chunking
- Creating Lists & Taking Notes
- Graphing & Charting
- Identifying Key Concepts
- Linking & Associations
- Visualizing
- Paraphrasing

The *Visual Memory* section has eight strategies that focus on improving memory of information that is written. Most of these activities require photocopying.

- Chunking
- Acronyms & Silly Sentences
- Defining & Drawing
- Graphing & Charting
- Identifying Key Concepts
- Visualizing
- Paraphrasing
- Saying, Tracing, Writing, & Drawing Sounds

Sample answers are provided in the Answer Key for some exercises. Accept any reasonable answer as correct.

The activities in this book will help your students improve and strengthen their memory skills. We hope that you and your students enjoy them!

Constance and Carolyn

Note: Throughout this book, all reported readability levels were analyzed with the Flesch-Kincaid Grade Level readability measure available in Microsoft Word. We used Microsoft Word 2003 SP2.

Enhancing Memory Skills

1. Have the student's hearing and vision checked by a physician and/or audiologist.

2. Help the student identify what to listen for or read for prior to presenting auditory information (e.g., who, what, where).

3. Present information in as many modalities as possible (e.g., auditory, visual, tactile).

4. Speak slowly to the student, using simple, concise statements.

5. Pause frequently to reinforce/check comprehension and retention while reading or listening to a story (e.g., characters, setting, problem, plot, details).

6. Ask the student to retell or paraphrase directions, instructions, or information presented.

7. Make sure the student has preferential seating (e.g., front row facing the board away from windows, doors, and possible distractions).

8. Reinforce good listening skills (e.g., eye contact, hands free, body facing speaker, eyes/ears on speaker).

9. Encourage the student to visualize or make pictures in his mind of what he is hearing or reading.

10. Have the student make checklists, charts, graphs, and/or diagrams, use To Do lists, and fill in homework planners and calendars.

Repeat! Repeat! Repeat!

Checking Up: Which Strategy Works Best for You?

Rate the effectiveness of the memory strategy after you have completed all of the tasks in that section.

Strategy _____

Circle the number that shows how helpful you feel the above strategy will be for you at school and/or at home.

    1 = not helpful
    5 = somewhat helpful, may use in the classroom or at home
  10 = very helpful, will use consistently in the classroom and at home

1   2   3   4   5   6   7   8   9   10

How will this strategy help you in the classroom?

_____

_____

_____

_____

How will this strategy help you outside the classroom?

_____

_____

_____

_____

Auditory Memory Pretest/Posttest

Indicate each correct answer with a **1**. Record the total number of correct answers at the end to determine percentage correct. For items 1-15, the student needs to repeat the information verbatim. See items 16-20 for the minimum number of items the student must recall to receive a point. Key items are underlined.

Read to student:
"I am going to read some numbers, words, sentences, and paragraphs to you. I want you to listen closely and try to remember as much as you can. After I read each one, I want you to say the information back to me. I can only read each item once. Do the best you can."

Student's Name:	Pretest Date	Posttest Date
1. 8, 6, 9, 2		
2. 3, 9, 1, 0, 5		
3. 10, 30, 60, 90, 40		
4. 5, 9, 6, 2, 3, 8, 0		
5. 8, 10, 7, 55, 6, 99, 2		
6. crib, bassinet, bottle, baby, blanket		
7. tree, flower, leaf, stem, petal, pollen, soil		
8. basket, lamp, book, cup, dog, sidewalk, candle		
9. dragon, ocean, dream, idea, think, sing, yellow		
10. movie, honor, generation, deliberate, join, garage, picture, print		
11. The young man read a book.		
12. Juan helped his grandmother bake a chocolate cake.		
13. Mr. Lee instructed his students to open their textbooks to page 32 and read the first two paragraphs to themselves.		

		Pretest Date	Posttest Date
14.	Electricity does not conduct well through rubber but travels easily through metal and water.		
15.	Marcia ran the Victoria Marathon in 3 hours and 30 minutes, her best time yet.		
16.	Marcelo is a nurse in an emergency room. He finds his job rewarding because he helps people feel better.	(5 items)	(5 items)
17.	Charles Darwin discovered the Galapagos Islands in the 1800s. These islands are located off the west coast of Ecuador in the Pacific Ocean.	(6 items)	(6 items)
18.	Molly and Dwayne needed to prepare for their chemistry final. They formed a study group with three other students in their chemistry class and reviewed their notes, textbook, and labs.	(7 items)	(7 items)
19.	To prepare for an earthquake, make sure you have an emergency kit. It should include a flashlight, radio, batteries, water, and non-perishable foods. Practice finding a safe location in your home to remain during an earthquake, such as under a sturdy table, in a doorway, or away from windows.	(8 items)	(8 items)
20.	Natasha wants to earn some extra money this summer. She loves the water and has decided to become a lifeguard. To qualify for a lifeguard position at the lake, Natasha must first pass the Red Cross lifesaving course, CPR, and First Aid. She must then submit an application and interview with the beach coordinator. Natasha is working hard toward her goal of being a lifeguard.	(8 items)	(8 items)
	Number Correct	/20	/20
	Percentage Correct	%	%

Comments: _____

_____

Strategies for Auditory Memory

Chunking: dividing a large group of words, numbers, or items into smaller units
Goal: *The student will learn to remember auditory information by breaking large groups of material into smaller, related units or categories.*

Creating Lists & Taking Notes: writing or recording information on paper
Goal: *The student will learn to remember auditory information by using a visual aid.*

Graphing & Charting: using visual graphs and charts to represent and organize information presented orally
Goal: *The student will learn to remember auditory information by using visual aids and organizers.*

Identifying Key Concepts: identifying the most important points of material presented orally
Goal: *The student will learn to remember information by selecting only the critical parts of material presented orally.*

Linking & Associations: identifying similar traits or characteristics that exist among lists, sequences, and directions
Goal: *The student will learn to remember auditory information by tying material together.*

Paraphrasing: restating material spoken aloud
Goal: *The student will learn to remember information presented orally by processing, comprehending, and paraphrasing material in her own words.*

Rehearsing & Subvocalizing: repeating words or sentences quietly to oneself
Goal: *The student will learn to remember words, sentences, lists, and notes presented orally through repeated exposure.*

Visualizing: using mental pictures to represent material presented orally
Goal: *The student will learn to remember auditory information by using more than one modality.*

Rehearsing & Subvocalizing

▶ **Goal:** *The student will learn to remember words, sentences, lists, and notes presented orally through repeated exposure.*

Ask the student to listen closely to each stimulus item in Exercises 1-10 on pages 15-24. Read each item aloud and have the student repeat it orally several times. Pause and ask the student to say it one final time. Eventually the student should be able to subvocalize (i.e., repeat the information silently to himself multiple times until memory is achieved) in his head.

There are three sections in each exercise.

Numbers

Words

Following Directions   (Note: Students are not expected to follow the directions, just repeat them. Students may follow the directions if they choose to.)

Exercise 1

▶ **Goal:** *The student will learn to remember words, sentences, lists, and notes presented orally through repeated exposure.*

Ask the student to listen closely to each stimulus item. Read each item aloud and have the student repeat it orally several times. Pause. Then have the student say it one final time. Eventually the student should be able to repeat the information in his head.

Numbers

1. 2, 6, 10
2. 8, 9, 7
3. 1, 9, 6
4. 4, 6, 9
5. 1, 8, 4

Words

1. red, blue, yellow
2. shirts, pants, shoes
3. apple, orange, banana
4. pencil, book, eraser
5. bike, ball, scooter

Following Directions

1. Point to the ceiling and point to the floor.
2. Touch your eyes and touch your toes.
3. Stand up and say the name of your school.
4. Say your mom's name and say your name.
5. Smile and lick your lips.

Exercise *2*

▶ **Goal:** *The student will learn to remember words, sentences, lists, and notes presented orally through repeated exposure.*

Ask the student to listen closely to each stimulus item. Read each item aloud and have the student repeat it orally several times. Pause. Then have the student say it one final time. Eventually the student should be able to repeat the information in his head.

Numbers

1. 1, 3, 5
2. 2, 4, 6
3. 6, 8, 12
4. 7, 9, 11
5. 11, 15, 18

Words

1. carrots, celery, lettuce
2. ring, necklace, bracelet
3. swimsuit, goggles, towel
4. rain, sleet, snow
5. floor, ceiling, wall

Following Directions

1. Stand up, turn around, and sit down.
2. Clap your hands, touch your nose, and say your name.
3. Smile, frown, and cough out loud.
4. Count to three, touch your toes, and blink your eyes.
5. Touch the door, touch the floor, and sit down.

Exercise 3

▶ **Goal:** *The student will learn to remember words, sentences, lists, and notes presented orally through repeated exposure.*

Ask the student to listen closely to each stimulus item. Read each item aloud and have the student repeat it orally several times. Pause. Then have the student say it one final time. Eventually the student should be able to repeat the information in his head.

Numbers

1. 2, 5, 8, 4
2. 5, 2, 0, 6
3. 3, 1, 9, 6
4. 7, 5, 3, 0
5. 3, 8, 9, 5

Words

1. blanket, sheet, pillow
2. bowl, cup, plate, glass
3. sofa, chair, table, lamp
4. finger, arm, head, toe
5. black, brown, green, blue

Following Directions

1. Put your elbow on the table, snap your fingers, and clap your hands.
2. Stomp your foot, jump up and down three times, and turn around four times.
3. Touch your left ear, touch your right ear, touch your nose, and touch your toes.
4. Jog in place, do a jumping jack, touch the ground, and sit down.
5. Close your eyes, nod your head, say your full name, and open your eyes.

Exercise 4

▶ **Goal:** *The student will learn to remember words, sentences, lists, and notes presented orally through repeated exposure.*

Ask the student to listen closely to each stimulus item. Read each item aloud and have the student repeat it orally several times. Pause. Then have the student say it one final time. Eventually the student should be able to repeat the information in his head.

Numbers

1. 2, 9, 3, 8
2. 6, 10, 2, 7
3. 3, 16, 5, 24
4. 21, 32, 43, 54
5. 60, 80, 70, 20

Words

1. sweater, jacket, glove, hat
2. hamburger, hot dog, milk shake, French fries
3. car, boat, motorcycle, airplane
4. street, sidewalk, path, road
5. bear, tiger, elephant, lion

Following Directions

1. Look up, look down, look to the right, and look to the left.
2. Raise your hand, touch your knee, say your name, and say your teacher's name.
3. Tap your toes, clap hands, smile, and snap your finger.
4. Tap your head, pat your stomach, hop on one foot, and sit down.
5. Count to five, touch your ears, cross your fingers, and name your favorite color.

Exercise 5

▶ **Goal:** *The student will learn to remember words, sentences, lists, and notes presented orally through repeated exposure.*

Ask the student to listen closely to each stimulus item. Read each item aloud and have the student repeat it orally several times. Pause. Then have the student say it one final time. Eventually the student should be able to repeat the information in his head.

Numbers

1. 12, 20, 32, 45
2. 37, 48, 66, 80
3. 4, 8, 16, 32
4. 21, 2, 1, 28
5. 50, 5, 60, 6

Words

1. bee, flag, book, ship
2. lemon, flower, chair, sun
3. shoe, cup, nose, pencil
4. candle, plate, paper, phone
5. spring, tree, up, tomorrow

Following Directions
(For items 4 and 5, the student will need a pencil.)

1. Open the door, close the door, touch the wall, and touch your chair.
2. Say your name, your favorite color, your teacher's name, and your favorite animal.
3. Give me "thumbs up," "thumbs down," turn around, and sit down.
4. Pick up a pencil, touch the eraser, put the pencil down, and touch the ground.
5. Say your name, give me "thumbs up," pick up a pencil, and touch the ground.

Exercise 6

▶ **Goal:** *The student will learn to remember words, sentences, lists, and notes presented orally through repeated exposure.*

Ask the student to listen closely to each stimulus item. Read each item aloud and have the student repeat it orally several times. Pause. Then have the student say it one final time. Eventually the student should be able to repeat the information in his head.

Numbers

1. 25, 8, 4, 2
2. 5, 2, 0, 6, 73
3. 3, 18, 9, 6, 4
4. 7, 51, 5, 3, 0
5. 3, 8, 99, 9, 5

Words

1. pillow, book, toy, bed
2. milk, shoe, boat, beach
3. run, jump, eat, rest
4. write, sit, swim, smile
5. happy, test, car, squirrel

Following Directions
(For the following items, the student will need a sheet of paper, a pen, and a pencil.)

1. Pick up the pencil. Write your name in the upper left corner of the paper and the date in the center.
2. Fold a sheet of paper in half. On the right side, draw a circle. On the left side, draw a square.
3. On your paper, draw a bird in a tree. Then draw a sun over the tree.
4. With your pen, draw a picture of your family. Then write each person's name underneath his or her picture.
5. Place your hand flat on your paper and spread open your fingers. Next trace your hand. Then make your picture into a turkey.

Exercise 7

▶ **Goal:** *The student will learn to remember words, sentences, lists, and notes presented orally through repeated exposure.*

Ask the student to listen closely to each stimulus item. Read each item aloud and have the student repeat it orally several times. Pause. Then have the student say it one final time. Eventually the student should be able to repeat the information in his head.

Numbers

1. 7, 3, 9, 4, 2, 7
2. 9, 6, 3, 1, 7, 8
3. 5, 3, 8, 6, 2, 4
4. 0, 6, 3, 8, 6, 5
5. 1, 9, 3, 7, 4, 2

Words

1. chart, umbrella, birthday, trash
2. dishwasher, chalk, type, computer
3. mouse, lime, drink, shop
4. excited, bat, cloud, study
5. giraffe, wander, discover, treasure

Following Directions

1. Open your math book to page 24, read the heading, and tell me what we are learning today.
2. Before lunch, finish workbook page 10 and turn it in to me.
3. While you listen to the presentation, take notes and write down questions.
4. To play the game, you will need a deck of cards, dice, and a timer.
5. To get an *A* in this class, you must listen, participate, and complete and turn in all assignments.

Exercise 8

▶ **Goal:** *The student will learn to remember words, sentences, lists, and notes presented orally through repeated exposure.*

Ask the student to listen closely to each stimulus item. Read each item aloud and have the student repeat it orally several times. Pause. Then have the student say it one final time. Eventually the student should be able to repeat the information in his head.

Numbers

1. 7, 8, 9, 3, 2, 6, 8
2. 4, 3, 1, 7, 9, 0, 1
3. 4, 5, 0, 9, 7, 1, 7
4. 2, 4, 1, 7, 6, 5, 3
5. 5, 3, 7, 9, 0, 1, 4

Words

1. game, sister, willow, buzz, flower
2. Dalmatian, principal, orange, football, honey
3. large, grades, achieve, serious, park
4. firefighter, hurricane, dangerous, rescue, safe
5. running, courage, strength, calm, lose

Following Directions

1. To wrap a gift, you will need wrapping paper, tape, scissors, a bow, and a card. Place the wrapping paper around the box and tape it. Cut off any extra paper. Then add the bow and the card.

2. Tonight, study for your biology test by reviewing class notes, skimming the chapter, and answering the chapter review questions.

3. To take good notes, be sure to use a title and date, record notes in an outline form, and write neatly.

4. For P.E. class tomorrow, bring running shoes, shorts, a T-shirt, and a water bottle.

5. To be prepared for class, students should have pens, pencils, paper, and completed homework.

Exercise 9

▶ **Goal:** *The student will learn to remember words, sentences, lists, and notes presented orally through repeated exposure.*

Ask the student to listen closely to each stimulus item. Read each item aloud and have the student repeat it orally several times. Pause. Then have the student say it one final time. Eventually the student should be able to repeat the information in his head.

Numbers

1. 2, 4, 6, 8, 3, 5, 7
2. 1, 9, 8, 3, 5, 6, 7
3. 0, 5, 2, 8, 4, 1, 3
4. 9, 5, 3, 2, 1, 8, 6
5. 8, 5, 7, 3, 2, 1, 4

Words

1. forest, country, map, driving, table
2. similar, novel, blue jay, shell, metaphor
3. simile, sing, hike, picnic, vacation
4. group, sunburn, surf, lavender, popular
5. hotel, basement, party, file, jogging

Following Directions

1. To write a book report, include the title, author, setting, character, problem, and resolution.
2. To write a paragraph, use a topic sentence, detail sentences with transitions, and a concluding sentence.
3. To edit a paper, remember COPS: Capitalization, Overall appearance, Punctuation, and Spelling.
4. To complete an experiment use the scientific method: form a question, make a prediction, conduct an experiment, record data, and draw conclusions.
5. To study for a test, review all class notes, skim through chapters, make a review sheet, and have a parent or friend quiz you on the information.

Exercise *10*

▶ **Goal:** *The student will learn to remember words, sentences, lists, and notes presented orally through repeated exposure.*

Ask the student to listen closely to each stimulus item. Read each item aloud and have the student repeat it orally several times. Pause. Then have the student say it one final time. Eventually the student should be able to repeat the information in his head.

Numbers

1. 92, 24, 57, 85, 21
2. 13, 43, 97, 64, 67
3. 29, 40, 86, 10, 47
4. 15, 95, 42, 31, 81
5. 19, 85, 25, 55, 20

Words

1. brave, recycle, career, dishonest, profit
2. wealth, clever, justify, excited, delighted
3. strong, biology, relaxing, object, independence
4. weekend, severe, careless, prevent, challenge
5. calm, decrease, relief, devastation, depend

Following Directions

1. Take out your science book, turn to page 128, answer questions 1-3, and define *life cycle*.

2. For math class today, take out your protractors and measure angles *a*, *b*, and *c* on Figure 1. Then turn in your paper to the box behind my desk.

3. Take our your social studies book. Choose one battle from the Civil War and write a short summary including who was involved, what occurred, and the outcome. Be prepared to share your summary with the class.

4. For your grammar assignment today, read the following sentences. Underline verbs, circle nouns, and correct spelling mistakes.

5. For your spelling assignment, write your list words in cursive, provide a synonym and an antonym for each word, and then use the spelling word in a sentence.

Chunking

▶ **Goal:** *The student will learn to remember auditory information by breaking large groups of material into smaller, related units or categories.*

One student may chunk information differently from another student. How a student chunks information depends on how that student remembers best. There is no right or wrong way to chunk information.

Use the following examples to show the student how to chunk a list of information into two (or more) groups based on category, pattern, sequence, association, or other method the student finds helpful. Two examples have more than one response to show that there is more than one way to chunk the information. Read each example aloud. Then have the student complete the exercises on pages 26-35. Each student should chunk the information in the exercises in whatever way makes the most sense to him.

Numbers
1. 2, 4, 6, 8
   Response: 2, 4 (pause) 6, 8
   These numbers are chunked based on the order the items were presented (sequence).
   The first two numbers are grouped together and the last two numbers are grouped together.

Words
1. spinach, cloud, butterfly, sand
   Response: spinach, sand (pause) cloud, butterfly
   These words are chunked based on the initial letter (e.g., *spinach* and *sand* both start with S
   and *cloud* and *butterfly* both start with letters at the beginning of the alphabet).

   Optional Response: spinach, cloud (pause) butterfly, sand
   These words are chunked based on the order the items were presented (sequence).

2. bee, book, see, cook, tree, hook
   Response: bee, see, tree (pause) book, cook, hook
   These words are chunked based on rhyming.

Following Directions   (Note: Students are not expected to follow the directions unless they want to.)
1. Touch your foot, touch your ear, touch your nose, touch your knee.
   Response: foot, knee (pause) ear, nose
   These directions are chunked based on category (e.g., *foot* and *knee* are part of the leg,
   ear and *nose* are part of the face).

   Optional Response: ear, nose (pause) knee, foot
   These directions are chunked based on sequence (e.g., placement in the body from top to bottom).

Exercise 1

▶ **Goal:** *The student will learn to remember auditory information by breaking large groups of material into smaller, related units or categories.*

Read the numbers, words, or directions aloud one at a time. Have the student repeat the information in chunks. Encourage the student to repeat the chunked items until memory is achieved.

Numbers

1. 1, 2, 3, 4
2. 2, 4, 6, 8
3. 5, 10, 15, 20
4. 10, 20, 30, 40
5. 1, 5, 2, 10

Words

1. sock, shoe, shirt, pants
2. apple, orange, red, blue
3. ball, bat, box, sand
4. tack, cat, back, sat
5. car, bus, street, road

Following Directions

1. Smile, frown, stand up, and sit down.
2. Touch your nose, touch your ear, touch your toes, and touch your knees.
3. Raise your hand, wave your hand, lift your foot, and wiggle your foot.
4. Touch your eyes, touch your head, touch your elbow, and touch your shoulder.
5. Stand up, turn around, sit down, and touch the ground.

Exercise 2

▶ **Goal:** *The student will learn to remember auditory information by breaking large groups of material into smaller, related units or categories.*

Read the numbers, words, or directions aloud one at a time. Have the student repeat the information in chunks. Encourage the student to repeat the chunked items until memory is achieved.

Numbers

1. 1, 5, 6, 8
2. 2, 6, 3, 9
3. 9, 3, 0, 5
4. 3, 2, 8, 4
5. 4, 0, 2, 9

Words

1. ball, book, shoe, coat
2. banana, pizza, orange, pen
3. fast, floor, door, last
4. pencil, phone, flower, candle
5. blanket, TV, radio, water

Following Directions

1. Smile, stand up, frown, and sit down.
2. Touch your nose, touch your toes, touch your ears, and touch your knees.
3. Raise your hand, lift your foot, wave your hand, and wiggle your foot.
4. Touch your eyes, touch your elbow, touch your head, and touch your shoulder.
5. Stand up, touch the ground, turn around, and sit down.

Exercise 3

▶ **Goal:** *The student will learn to remember auditory information by breaking large groups of material into smaller, related units or categories.*

Read the numbers, words, or directions aloud one at a time. Have the student repeat the information in chunks. Encourage the student to repeat the chunked items until memory is achieved.

Numbers

1. 0, 1, 11, 12
2. 12, 14, 2, 4
3. 8, 9, 16, 19
4. 3, 7, 19, 10
5. 49, 38, 21, 10

Words

1. chair, vase, flower, desk
2. lettuce, tomato, bread, rolls
3. coffee, dinner, lunch, tea
4. light, night, who, boo
5. ship, car, automobile, boat

Following Directions

1. Say your first name, say your last name, stand up, and sit down.
2. Hop on one foot, jump up and down, touch the ground, and touch your chair.
3. Point to the door, touch the door, point to a book, and touch a paper.
4. Say hello, say goodbye, name your favorite color, and name your lucky number.
5. Tap your finger on the table, hold up two fingers, point to your foot, and touch your shoe.

Exercise 4

▶ **Goal:** *The student will learn to remember auditory information by breaking large groups of material into smaller, related units or categories.*

Read the numbers, words, or directions aloud one at a time. Have the student repeat the information in chunks. Encourage the student to repeat the chunked items until memory is achieved.

Numbers

1. 1, 10, 2, 20
2. 2, 14, 6, 18
3. 20, 12, 13, 19
4. 3, 15, 12, 7
5. 60, 35, 70, 45

Words

1. camera, shoe, computer, telephone
2. strawberry, light bulb, crib, sweater
3. Halloween, truck, candy, refrigerator
4. magazine, dress, lamp, picture
5. bee, see, purse, tree

Following Directions

1. Jump up, touch your nose, smile, and turn around.
2. Close your eyes, touch your knees, stand up, and touch the ground.
3. Say your name, count to five, smile, and frown.
4. Raise your right hand, make a fist, clap your hands, and close your eyes.
5. Look left, nod your head, raise your hand, and fold your hands together.

Exercise 5

▶ **Goal:** *The student will learn to remember auditory information by breaking large groups of material into smaller, related units or categories.*

Read the numbers, words, or directions aloud one at a time. Have the student repeat the information in chunks. Encourage the student to repeat the chunked items until memory is achieved.

Numbers

1. 0, 15, 21, 35
2. 52, 34, 12, 14
3. 81, 91, 6, 90
4. 33, 77, 18, 20
5. 99, 28, 21, 11

Words

1. pot, lid, handle, stairs
2. bleach, smell, cheese, wash
3. won, race, run, face
4. sweet, sugar, lemon, yellow
5. smile, family, zipper, soft

Following Directions

1. Hold up your pinkie finger, give a "thumbs up," tap your right toe, and stand up.
2. Stretch up tall, stand up, turn around four times, and look at my eyes.
3. Say "Hi," say "Stir fry," say "Slow down," and say "Turn around."
4. Turn to a neighbor, ask for his/her favorite color, repeat it to me, and stand up.
5. Tap your chair, walk to the door and touch the knob, nod your head, and tap the table.

Exercise 6

▶ **Goal:** *The student will learn to remember auditory information by breaking large groups of material into smaller, related units or categories.*

Read the numbers, words, or directions aloud one at a time. Have the student repeat the information in chunks. Encourage the student to repeat the chunked items until memory is achieved.

Numbers

1. 70, 43, 52, 25
2. 94, 17, 86, 76
3. 11, 71, 62, 97
4. 29, 51, 23, 20
5. 100, 38, 27, 81

Words

1. TV, movies, deck, patio, yard
2. electricity, gas, cooking, oil, driving
3. book, sleep, eat, desk, study
4. tomorrow, today, several, yesterday, many
5. excited, frown, disappointed, sad, smile

Following Directions

1. Pretend to drink a glass of water, say your address, and puff out your cheeks.
2. Raise both arms in the air, tell me about a place you would like to visit, and shake my hand.
3. Say four words that rhyme with *play*, tell me your birth date, and say the months of the year.
4. Count by fives to 40, name three books, and tap your foot on the ground four times.
5. Describe something that is scary, name one holiday, tell me how many months in a year, and put both hands on the table.

Exercise 7

▶ **Goal:** *The student will learn to remember auditory information by breaking large groups of material into smaller, related units or categories.*

Read the numbers, words, or directions aloud one at a time. Have the student repeat the information in chunks. Encourage the student to repeat the chunked items until memory is achieved.

Numbers

1. 1, 2, 3, 4, 5, 6
2. 2, 4, 6, 1, 3, 5
3. 10, 20, 30, 60, 80
4. 5, 10, 15, 25, 30, 35
5. 3, 6, 9, 15, 18, 21

Words

1. apple, pizza, hamburger, orange, French fries, grapes
2. dock, cane, sock, lock, train, plane
3. book, TV, movie, paper, radio, pencil
4. street, state, city, avenue, road, country
5. chair, sofa, towel, sheet, table, napkin

Following Directions

1. Listen to the following story and write the names of the characters and the setting on a sheet of paper.
2. Take out a sheet of notebook paper, number the paper 1-10, and write down ten things you learned in science class today.
3. After watching the short video, write a two-sentence summary.
4. For social studies class tomorrow, please bring an article about current events.
5. For language arts homework, read Chapters 1-3 and answer questions 1-10 in your journal.

Exercise 8

▶ **Goal:** *The student will learn to remember auditory information by breaking large groups of material into smaller, related units or categories.*

Read the numbers, words, or directions aloud one at a time. Have the student repeat the information in chunks. Encourage the student to repeat the chunked items until memory is achieved.

Numbers

1. 110, 115, 130, 135
2. 31, 34, 32, 44, 46
3. 87, 91, 22, 32, 62
4. 13, 56, 22, 30, 50
5. 99, 38, 24, 17, 27

Words

1. speakers, car, truck, stereo, bike
2. computer, paper, pencil, type, pen
3. pool, bowling, water, games, swim
4. cup, sow, cow, bow, up
5. window, fall, sill, open, close

Following Directions

1. List three sports, cross your fingers, put your elbows on the table, and put your fingers in your ears.
2. Make a fist, give yourself a high five, put your hands on your hips, and look over your left shoulder.
3. Pretend to make a phone call, laugh out loud, smile twice, and cross your arms.
4. Stand up, walk to the door, do four jumping jacks, and turn around three times.
5. Blink your eyes six times, show me three fingers, point to me, and share a funny story.

Exercise 9

▶ **Goal:** *The student will learn to remember auditory information by breaking large groups of material into smaller, related units or categories.*

Read the numbers, words, or directions aloud one at a time. Have the student repeat the information in chunks. Encourage the student to repeat the chunked items until memory is achieved.

Numbers

1. 12, 70, 31, 15, 29, 40
2. 9, 80, 45, 67, 29, 4
3. 31, 13, 40, 83, 90, 68
4. 24, 35, 6, 98, 56, 8
5. 10, 76, 50, 30, 41, 9

Words

1. letters, phone, raspberry, towel, snow, hat
2. table, shoe, basket, book, lamp, phone
3. park, grass, street, television, computer, candle
4. ball, lemon, tree, magazine, water, music
5. fire, picture, scissors, raisin, garbage, door

Following Directions

1. Open your book to page 4, grab your pencil, and write your name at the top of your paper.
2. Turn to page 23, read the first paragraph, and write a one-sentence summary.
3. Pick up your pencil, write your name in the top left corner of your paper, and then write your teacher's name in the top right corner.
4. Do the even numbers on pages 14 and 15 in your math workbook and the odd numbers on pages 12-13 in your social studies workbook.
5. For homework, write a descriptive paragraph in your language arts notebook and write 10 sentences about the history of the Constitution in your social studies notebook.

Exercise *10*

▶ **Goal:** *The student will learn to remember auditory information by breaking large groups of material into smaller, related units or categories.*

Read the numbers, words, or directions aloud one at a time. Have the student repeat the information in chunks. Encourage the student to repeat the chunked items until memory is achieved.

Numbers

1. 88, 78, 60, 51, 62, 63
2. 150, 175, 110, 112, 113
3. 200, 190, 180, 121, 120
4. 105, 107, 110, 120, 125
5. 63, 126, 252, 126, 120

Words

1. biology, Washington, algebra, color, novel
2. life, governor, equation, texture, page
3. science, solve, first, medium, character
4. study, general, variable, strict, plot
5. conflict, shade, numeral, victory, grow

Following Directions

1. Define the word *complete*, name a synonym for *thrilled*, and tell me how to spell the word *study*.

2. Tell me how you study for a test, list one way to organize information, and define *rough draft*.

3. Tell me what to put in a heading, identify how to end a letter, list how many sentences are in a paragraph, and define *topic sentence*.

4. Name one way to study for a test, define the word *anxiety*, tell me how many days ahead you should study for a test, and name your hardest class.

5. Define *edit*, define *conclusion*, define *supporting sentence*, and name four items you check when you edit.

Creating Lists & Taking Notes

▶ **Goal:** *The student will learn to remember auditory information by using a visual aid.*

Give the student paper and a pen or pencil. Use the examples below to show the student how to make a list (e.g., using bullets) and take notes.

Read the passages in the exercises on pages 37-46 to the student. As you read each one aloud, have the student create a list, message, or note. Repeat information as needed. Then ask the student to repeat what he has written.

1. Samir and his mother went to the grocery store to buy food for his birthday dinner. Samir wanted spaghetti and meatballs. They need to buy spaghetti, hamburger, spaghetti sauce, bread, and salad.

   Shopping list:
   spaghetti
   hamburger
   spaghetti sauce
   bread
   salad

2. You will need the following materials for Social Studies class this year: one 3-ring notebook, two folders with pockets, a package of lined paper, pens, and pencils.

   • one 3-ring notebook
   • two folders with pockets
   • package of lined paper
   • pens
   • pencils

2. "Hi, Mr. Wolf. This is Rebecca calling about babysitting Saturday night. I'm sorry but I can't babysit on Saturday because I have a big science project due on Monday and I have to work on it all weekend."

   Rebecca can't babysit Saturday night.

Exercise *1*

▶ **Goal:** *The student will learn to remember auditory information by using a visual aid.*

Grocery Lists

Read each passage aloud. Have the student create a list using the information. Then have the student repeat the information.

1. When you go to the market today, please pick up some fresh blueberries, lettuce, and one cucumber.

2. Please pick up six boneless, skinless chicken breasts; hamburger meat; and hamburger buns. We are having the Millers over for dinner tonight and plan to grill on the barbecue.

3. After school, Karen and her mom went to the grocery store to buy treats for the students in Karen's classroom. It was Karen's birthday tomorrow and she wanted to bring food to class to celebrate. At the store, they bought carrot sticks, cheese, crackers, cookies, and juice.

4. Jordan's town had a farmer's market every weekend in the summer. Jordan and his two older sisters went every Saturday morning to buy fresh produce for their family. This week, Jordan's mother asked him to bring home a carton of strawberries, a whole pineapple, half a cantaloupe, and a bag of Macintosh apples.

5. The Smith family likes to go grocery shopping on Sundays. The five of them, Mrs. Smith, Mr. Smith, Joe, Tanya, and Brittney, pile into the car around 9:00 a.m. and head to the nearest Safeway. Each member is given a list of items to find. This week, Joe had to find Cheerios, oatmeal, maple syrup, microwave popcorn, and Pop Tarts.

Exercise 2

▶ **Goal:** *The student will learn to remember auditory information by using a visual aid.*

Phone Messages

Read each passage aloud. Have the student create a message or note using the information. Then have the student repeat the information.

1. This is a message for Sean. This is Mrs. Bellows calling from Sunset Elementary. Your library books are two weeks overdue. Please return them to school.

2. Hello. This message is for Mrs. Spring. This is Anne calling from Delaney's Department Store letting Mrs. Spring know that her glass vase has arrived and she can pick it up anytime this week.

3. Hi, Lee Family. This is your next door neighbor, Mrs. Sung, calling to invite you over for a barbecue on Sunday afternoon. Please let us know if you are able to attend.

4. Hello, Thomas, this is Coach Wittman calling to let you know that soccer practice has been cancelled for today due to the thunderstorms. There will be a makeup practice on Wednesday from 3-5 p.m., weather permitting.

5. Hi, Ian, it's Natalia calling from Mr. Peterson's class. I was wondering if you could tell me what tonight's homework is for science class. Please call me at 456-0099. Thanks.

Exercise 3

▶ **Goal:** *The student will learn to remember auditory information by using a visual aid.*

Chores

Read each passage aloud. Have the student create a list using the information. Then have the student repeat the information.

1. Crystal's mother posted her weekly chores on the refrigerator. This week, Crystal is in charge of taking out the garbage and emptying the dishwasher.

2. Before noon, Ashley needs to make her bed, straighten her room, take out the garbage, and vacuum the upstairs carpets.

3. Charlotte and her brother, Justin, have daily chores. Charlotte is in charge of feeding the cats and making her bed while Justin has to take out the trash and recycling.

4. Heidi's mom was preparing for a dinner party. She instructed Heidi to vacuum the kitchen and dining room floors, wipe the counters, set the table, cut the vegetables, and prepare the appetizers.

5. Five students are selected each week in Mr. Grubbs' fifth-grade class to be room helpers. Each student is assigned a different duty. This week, Tom, Dana, Kevin, Charlie, and Jada were chosen. Tom was in charge of cleaning the whiteboard. Dana had to pick up any trash from the floor. Kevin had to make sure all the chairs were pushed into the desks. Charlie was in charge of feeding the hamsters. Jada's duties included collecting homework and recycling paper.

Exercise 4

▶ **Goal:** *The student will learn to remember auditory information by using a visual aid.*

Following Directions

Read each passage aloud. Have the student create a list or note using the information. Then have the student repeat the information.

1. To get to Barber's Department Store, take a left at the light. Remain on that road for one mile. Turn right on Sunnyside Street. Barber's is on the left.

2. Mrs. Milly led her class on a walk to the park. To get to the park, she and the students walked for a quarter of a mile on Lumber Street. Next they took a left at the light onto Newberry Lane. Finally they turned right onto Apple Way and found the beautiful park.

3. To get to the library from Mr. Hall's sixth-grade classroom, go down D Wing and take a right once you reach F Wing. Walk past the principal's office and take a left at the end of the hall. The library is on the right side.

4. Shaneese and Angela decided to hike to the hot springs for a swim. They drove to the entrance of Glover's Park where the hike began. Once there, they put on their hiking shoes and began their trek. First they walked one mile along the flat path. When they reached a fork, they followed the sign that was marked *Hot Springs*. They walked down a long, winding hill for about three-fourths of a mile until they reached the bottom. At the bottom, they found the hot springs.

5. After school, I need you to drive your brother to tennis practice. From our house, it should take about 20 minutes. Go east on Bradley Road. Take a right at the light onto Portal Boulevard. Remain on Portal for 5 miles. When you see Missy's Spaghetti Factory, turn left. The Newplan Tennis Club should be on your immediate right side.

Exercise 5

▶ **Goal:** *The student will learn to remember auditory information by using a visual aid.*

Recipes

Read each passage aloud. Have the student create a list or note using the information. Then have the student repeat the information.

1. To make tomato soup, mix the soup with one can of water in a bowl. Microwave the bowl on high for three minutes. Let it sit for one minute, then stir and serve.

2. To make instant hot cocoa, heat 6 ounces of water in a microwave or on a stove until hot. Stir in one envelope of hot cocoa mix.

3. To make rice for two people, put 1 and ¼ cup water into a pot and bring to a boil. Stir in one cup of rice. Reduce heat, cover the pot, and let simmer for 10 minutes or until the water is absorbed. Remove from heat and serve.

4. To make oatmeal, you will need 1 cup of water, ½ cup oats, and a dash of salt. Bring water and salt to a boil in a pot, then stir in oats and let simmer for 3-5 minutes. Cover and remove from heat.

5. To make a quick chili dinner, you will need 1 pound of ground beef or turkey, 2 cans of tomato sauce, 1 packet of chili seasoning, and 1 can of kidney beans. First brown the beef or turkey. Then stir in one packet of chili seasoning, tomato sauce, and kidney beans. Bring to a boil, cover, and simmer for 10 minutes.

Exercise 6

▶ **Goal:** *The student will learn to remember auditory information by using a visual aid.*

Read each passage aloud. Have the student create a list or note using the information. Then have the student repeat the information.

1. To get to the park, turn right on Martin Street, walk three blocks and follow Park Street another three blocks. It takes about five or ten minutes to get to the park, depending on how quickly you walk.

2. When you go to the grocery store, please get hand soap, yogurt, bread, lunch meat, lettuce, tomatoes, and an avocado.

3. Please be sure to bring your lab notebook, lab coat, safety glasses, and periodic table to class tomorrow. Forgotten items will result in lower grades.

4. Be sure to have all of the math problems done by tomorrow. The assignment may seem like a lot but it won't take too long. Textbook: page 201, 1-8 evens; page 203, 11-19 odds; page 204, 1-18 all; and workbook, page 37, 10-12. This is due tomorrow.

5. To get an *A* on this paper, you must turn in an outline, a rough draft, a peer review, and a typed final draft.

Exercise 7

▶ **Goal:** *The student will learn to remember auditory information by using a visual aid.*

Read each passage aloud. Have the student create a list, message, or note using the information. Then have the student repeat the information.

1. The best pizza is from Zack's in Rockridge. Call 555-3567 before 5:30 p.m. and order take-out. Try one of their specials or one of their calzones.

2. Please call and make your airline reservations today. We need to depart out of SeaTac on Wednesday, April 1st at 9 a.m. Try to get a direct flight to Madison. We need to leave Madison on Sunday, April 5th at 5 p.m. The number for the reservations desk is 800-555-5897.

3. To hike to the summit, head north on the Grace Trail for half a mile. Then head west on the Dunn Trail for 4 miles. When you get to the split, head to the right and walk another 100 yards. If you want the best view, carefully climb up the south side of the big, black rock.

4. Tomorrow I need you to pick up the shirts and pants at the cleaners, drop the dog off at the groomer at noon, return the library books at the main branch, and then pick up the dog at 1:30 p.m.

5. We're going to see a movie at 7:10 p.m. It gets out around 9:00 p.m., and then we're going to go bowling. Then we're going to Ian's house to sleep over. I'll be home by 10 a.m. tomorrow. If you need to call, you'll know where I am. It's hard to hear in the bowling alley, so leave a message if I don't answer my cell.

Exercise 8

▶ **Goal:** *The student will learn to remember auditory information by using a visual aid.*

Read each passage aloud. Have the student create a list, message, or note using the information. Then have the student repeat the information.

1. Guess what? We are finally getting a puppy! Remember, you promised to feed the puppy in the morning and night, walk her once a day, help train her, and play with her after school.

2. As you read the story, try to visualize, or make a picture of the words. Remember to use who, what, where, when, color, size, number, shape, texture, sound, movement, and mood when describing or visualizing a picture.

3. If you want to make burritos tonight, you'll have to stop by the store. Get tortillas, lean ground beef or chicken, cheese, vegetarian refried beans, lettuce, tomatoes, salsa, avocados, and corn. Try to be home by 6, okay?

4. Your homework tonight includes: history: read chapter 11, section 1 and be ready for a possible pop quiz; math: pages 76-77, problems 12-24, grammar worksheet problems 11-14, and study for a science quiz on bones. Make a homework attack plan that lists the assignments you must complete in the order that you will complete them.

5. To study for the final exam adequately, begin a week ahead of time. Collect and review all of your past tests and quizzes, complete all chapter reviews in the book, complete the class review, make your own review notes, and study, study, study each night. You must decide what to do each night.

Exercise 9

▶ **Goal:** *The student will learn to remember auditory information by using a visual aid.*

Read each passage aloud. Have the student create a list, message, or note using the information. Then have the student repeat the information.

1. Please be sure to empty the dishwasher, take out the garbage, water the plants, and pick up your room before you walk over to Samantha's house.

2. Once you get into groups, decide who will conduct the research, write the report, create visual aids, and present the final project to the class.

3. To make a tasty pizza, you need crust, sauce, mozzarella cheese, sausage, pepperoni, mushrooms, and green pepper. Preheat the oven to 450 degrees. Spread the sauce on the crust. Then put the rest of the ingredients on in any order. Bake for about 15 minutes or until the crust is golden brown.

4. Hi, there. Please tell your mom that I can drive car pool this Tuesday at 7 a.m. if she can drive car pool on Wednesday at 7 a.m. Have her call me back to confirm she received the message. The number is 555-1256.

5. You have a science test tomorrow, a math assignment (page 145, problems 10-13), and 30 minutes of reading. Make a homework attack plan that lists the assignments you must complete in the order you plan to complete them. Also include break times and meals. Remember, you do not have to do all of your studying at one time. In fact, I recommend you take 5-minute breaks to stand up, go to the bathroom, or grab a drink every 20-30 minutes.

Exercise 10

▶ **Goal:** *The student will learn to remember auditory information by using a visual aid.*

Read each passage aloud. Have the student create a list, message, or note using the information. Then have the student repeat the information.

1. If you want to go to Benson Heights for the weekend with your friends, you have to help me clean the house today. You need to dust the furniture, clean out the refrigerator, water the plants, vacuum the family room, strip the beds, wash the sheets, and remake the beds. It should take you less than three hours if you work hard.

2. To bake potatoes, preheat the oven to 350 degrees. Get four potatoes and scrub them in the sink with a brush. Carefully poke a few little holes in the skins with a fork. Then place them in the oven for 45 minutes to an hour.

3. Your science projects must include a question, a hypothesis, a list of supplies and materials, an experiment, data, observations, and conclusions. I expect to see a typed-up report and at least one visual aid. Questions and hypothesis are due next Wednesday. I will give you more due dates tomorrow.

4. Barclay's is a tasty restaurant. If you go, order the grilled artichoke as an appetizer. Be sure to order their raspberry iced tea to drink. I would recommend the cheddar and avocado burger or the chicken Cobb salad and the apple crisp for dessert.

5. To get to the hotel in Tahoe City from your house, enter onto East I-80 at South Van Ness Avenue in San Francisco, heading toward Sacramento. When you get near Sacramento, watch for signs to Reno. Continue on I-80 east toward Reno. In Truckee, exit onto north highway 89 and continue about 13 miles. When you reach Tahoe City, take a left after the light. The hotel is on Main Street.

Graphing & Charting

▶ **Goal:** *The student will learn to remember auditory information by using visual aids and organizers.*

Give the student paper and a pen or pencil. Show the student the pages of graphing examples on pages 189-193. Then have the student listen to the information and make her own graph, chart, or diagram.

Initially read the information aloud once and have the student identify the most appropriate chart, graph, or diagram to best display the information. Then repeat the information so the student can construct the graph, chart, or diagram to represent and organize the material.

Exercise 1

▶ **Goal:** *The student will learn to remember auditory information by using visual aids and organizers.*

Read the information in each item once to the student. Have the student identify the appropriate graph, chart, or diagram to use. Then repeat the information so the student can construct the graph, chart, or diagram to represent and organize the material.

1. Things to do in winter / Things to do in summer

   ice skate
   swim
   ski
   have picnics
   play at the park
   read a book
   build a snowman
   go sledding
   drink hot chocolate
   go to a movie
   drink lemonade
   ride a bike

2. Character: Matilda
   Description: young girl   liked by her classmates
                 very smart   tall
                 teacher's pet   plays practical jokes on parents
                 silly parents   very patient

3. Mrs. Simon's fourth-grade class had a week-long magazine sale. The following shows how many magazines the students sold on each day of the week.

   Monday = 20 magazines
   Tuesday= 35 magazines
   Wednesday = 66 magazines
   Thursday = 55 magazines
   Friday = 73 magazines

Exercise 2

▶ **Goal:** *The student will learn to remember auditory information by using visual aids and organizers.*

Read the information in each item once to the student. Have the student identify the appropriate graph, chart, or diagram to use. Then repeat the information so the student can construct the graph, chart, or diagram to represent and organize the material.

1. **Tropical Rainforests**
   a type of habitat
   wet
   receive heavy rainfall
   close to the equator
   get lots of sunlight and warmth
   trees grow to gigantic size
   trees have dark, green leathery leaves
   in Central and South America, west
       and central Africa, southeast Asia

   Deserts
   a type of habitat
   dry places
   little water
   few plants or animals
   warm days, cold nights
   in North Africa, southwest Africa, India,
       Australia, central Asia

2. Kim and Alex are members of their school's swim team. For one week, they counted the number of laps they swam each day.

   Monday = 120 laps
   Tuesday = 134 laps
   Wednesday = 119 laps
   Thursday = 150 laps
   Friday = 145 laps

3. Mr. Delphi's sixth-grade class was instructed to brainstorm about the topic of environmental pollution. The class generated the following responses:

trash	radioactive gases
carcinogens	toxins
waste	toxic emissions
lead	gasoline
acid rain	pesticides
carbon dioxide	poison

Exercise 3

▶ **Goal:** *The student will learn to remember auditory information by using visual aids and organizers.*

Read the information in each item once to the student. Have the student identify the appropriate graph, chart, or diagram to use. Then repeat the information so the student can construct the graph, chart, or diagram to represent and organize the material.

1. Joanne's father owned a pet store. During the month of August, 20% of the store's profit came from fish sales, 15% came from cat sales, 40% came from dog sales, and the remainder came from the sales of supplies. What percentage did Joanne's father make from pet store supplies?

2. Frogs and toads have similar and dissimilar characteristics. Both frogs and toads have a brain and are amphibians. They also both hatch from eggs, and have a backbone and a heart. Unlike toads, frogs have smooth, slimy skin; bulging eyes; and teeth. Toads, on the other hand, have dry, wart-like skin. They have no teeth and can walk.

3. Cinderella, the stepsisters, and the Prince are some of the main characters in the fairy tale, *Cinderella*. Cinderella is a lovely, young girl with blonde hair who is forced to dress in rags. Her stepsisters are evil, selfish, ugly, and clumsy. The prince is handsome, nice, and determined to find Cinderella.

Exercise 4

▶ **Goal:** *The student will learn to remember auditory information by using visual aids and organizers.*

Read the information in each item once to the student. Have the student identify the appropriate graph, chart, or diagram to use. Then repeat the information so the student can construct the graph, chart, or diagram to represent and organize the material.

1. The word *happy* has many synonyms. Among them are: *glad, delighted, pleased, tickled, excited, content, joyful,* and *cheerful.*

2. Dolphins are mammals. All dolphins have a beak-like snout and sharp, pointed teeth. Most dolphins are about six feet in length. The largest is the bottle-nose dolphin. This dolphin may reach up to nine feet in length. Dolphins are predators and feed on live food except when trained otherwise. Their primary food source is fish.

3. Kiplin Middle School had a bake sale to raise money for their basketball and volleyball teams. The sixth grade, with 171 students, raised $98. The 168 seventh-grade students raised $75, and the 185 eighth-grade students raised a total of $112. Which grade raised the least money?

Exercise 5

▶ **Goal:** *The student will learn to remember auditory information by using visual aids and organizers.*

Read the information in each item once to the student. Have the student identify the appropriate graph, chart, or diagram to use. Then repeat the information so the student can construct the graph, chart, or diagram to represent and organize the material.

1. California has four main regions: the temperate coastal region, the Central Valley, the desert, and the mountains. The first settlers were the Native Americans, followed by Spanish, Russian, and Mexican settlers. The English also settled in California. The state became popular during the late 1840s because of the Gold Rush. California became the 31st state in 1850.

2. Student council elections were held last week at Benfield School. Only 100 students voted. The following are the results of the election: 20% of the students voted for Karen Baker, 42% voted for Jordan Smith, 13% voted for Jon Kim, and 25% voted for Bella Graham.

3. The word *difficult* has many synonyms and antonyms. The following are synonyms for *difficult*: *arduous, hard, laborious, serious, tough, uphill*, and *effortful*. The following are antonyms of *difficult*: *easy, simple, calm, plain, effortless*, and *facile*.

Exercise 6

▶ **Goal:** *The student will learn to remember auditory information by using visual aids and organizers.*

Read the information in each item once to the student. Have the student identify the appropriate graph, chart, or diagram to use. Then repeat the information so the student can construct the graph, chart, or diagram to represent and organize the material.

1. Five girls stood next to each other for a picture. The photographer looked at the girls. Sadie stood next to Mandy. Amanda stood next to neither girl. Mandy was on the end. Natasha put her right arm around Amanda's shoulder. The girls all squeezed in, squishing Jordan in the middle. All of the girls smiled. Who stood next to whom?

2. The class was divided over what class pet to get. Thirty-five percent of the class wanted a turtle and 20 percent thought a frog was a better idea. Thirteen percent voted for a hamster because they thought a rodent would be more cuddly. Eleven percent of the students preferred fish for class pet. Nine percent asked for a snake, which the teacher objected to. Eight percent voted for a spider and the remaining four percent really wanted an ant farm. In the end, the clear winner was the turtle. The teacher was relieved.

3. From January to June, Lindsay's savings account showed the following totals at the end of each month: January – $1200, February – $1500, March – $1600, April – $1700, May – $1100, and June – $1400.

Exercise 7

▶ **Goal:** *The student will learn to remember auditory information by using visual aids and organizers.*

Read the information in each item once to the student. Have the student identify the appropriate graph, chart, or diagram to use. Then repeat the information so the student can construct the graph, chart, or diagram to represent and organize the material.

1. Mr. Jacobson needed to keep track of the latest test grades on a chart. No one got an *A* plus. Eighteen percent of the class got *A*s, two percent got *A* minuses, ten percent got *B* pluses, 20 percent got *B*s, and eight percent got *B* minuses. Twenty-two percent got *C* pluses, ten percent got *C*s. No one got a *C* minus. Ten percent of the students got *D*s.

   Extra credit: If there are 50 students in Mr. Jacobson's class, how many students received each grade?

2. I decided to go on a long bike ride. On the first day, I biked east 60 miles from North Bend over Ellensberg to Roslyn. Then I rode further east and then north another 60 miles over Blewett Pass to Leavenworth. In Leavenworth, I stopped at a hotel where I swam and relaxed at the pool, had dinner, and got a good night's sleep. The next morning, I got up early to beat the heat. I rode 70 miles west over Stevens Pass to Carnation. Although the ride was tough at times, I saw some gorgeous scenery.

3. Kevin and Leslie are searching for a new house. They need to put together a list of house requirements for their realtor. Kevin wants something close to work and friends, but Leslie prefers being close to a gym and hiking trails. Leslie loves to garden, and Kevin enjoys working in his shop and doing projects around the house. Both want a house with lots of light that is near shops and restaurants.

Exercise 8

▶ **Goal:** *The student will learn to remember auditory information by using visual aids and organizers.*

Read the information in each item once to the student. Have the student identify the appropriate graph, chart, or diagram to use. Then repeat the information so the student can construct the graph, chart, or diagram to represent and organize the material.

1. The story Maria wrote features her sister, Josephina, as the main character. The story is set in Denver, Colorado in present times. The problem is that Josephina has lost her dog. First Josephina looks in the neighbor's yard. Then she asks her friend, Kimi, to help her look for the lost pet. They search in the park and at school. Finally they find the dog asleep in the laundry basket! Josephina is relieved.

2. The two vacations I took this summer were both fun and relaxing. In June, I went to Lake Chelan in Washington state. My family took our boat and we camped at a place called Deer Point. Every day we water skied in the lake and hiked on the hills. The temperatures were in the 90s every day. Luckily the water was cold and refreshing. In July, my family went to the San Juan Islands in Washington state for two weeks. We took our boat again but stayed in a hotel in Deer Harbor. During the day, we went on picnics, looked for crabs, and went fishing. The weather was cooler, in the 70s, but we still spent lots of time outside. I swam in the pool every day. I hope we do both vacations again next year.

3. Mr. Fong's doctor asked him to keep track of what he ate in a food journal. In the morning, he ate scrambled eggs and whole wheat toast for breakfast and drank a glass of orange juice. He had a cup of coffee and a blueberry muffin for a 10 o'clock snack. For lunch, he had a chicken sandwich with jack cheese, lettuce, and tomato on a sourdough roll, French fries, and a cola. At three o'clock, Mr. Fong ate a chocolate bar and a bag of corn chips. For dinner, he had a large piece of halibut, white rice, broccoli, and a salad with cucumber and carrots. For dessert, Mr. Fong had a piece of chocolate cake with frosting.

Auditory Memory: Graphing & Charting
No-Glamour Memory

55

Copyright © 2007 LinguiSystems, Inc.

Exercise 9

▶ **Goal:** *The student will learn to remember auditory information by using visual aids and organizers.*

Read the information in each item once to the student. Have the student identify the appropriate graph, chart, or diagram to use. Then repeat the information so the student can construct the graph, chart, or diagram to represent and organize the material.

1. An expository essay differs from a persuasive essay in several ways. An expository essay tells a story, but a persuasive essay tries to convince the reader of an opinion. Expository essays are written in first or third person, and persuasive essays can be written in first, second, or third person. Expository essays do not express opinions but persuasive essays do. Both are fun to write, though.

2. The story *Harry Potter and the Sorcerer's Stone* by J.K. Rowling, is about Harry, who is forced to live with his mean aunt, uncle, and cousin in England after his parents die. On his 11th birthday, Harry receives a letter stating that he has been accepted to attend a school called *Hogwarts*. Harry soon learns that Hogwarts, a school for witches and wizards, is a much better place to live than with his aunt and uncle. Ron Weasley and Hermoine Granger become his best friends at school. They help him overcome a three-headed dog to retrieve a highly-guarded object.

3. For the field trip, please remember the following things. Be at school tomorrow morning at 7. Bring rain jackets and boots to keep dry as well as a backpack with at least 10 sheets of lined paper in a large zipper bag with a pen and a pencil, and a bag lunch. Everyone must select a partner and stay with that person. Stay seated on the bus and be polite to all adults. I hope this field trip runs smoothly so we can do more of these later this year.

Exercise 10

▶ **Goal:** *The student will learn to remember auditory information by using visual aids and organizers.*

Read the information in each item once to the student. Have the student identify the appropriate graph, chart, or diagram to use. Then repeat the information so the student can construct the graph, chart, or diagram to represent and organize the material.

1. Sam had three projects due for school and she needed supplies for each one. For science, she needed a large piece of particle board, two pounds of plaster, nails, light and dark blue paint, white paint, green paint, and a black permanent pen. For math, she needed string, nails, tape, and a small piece of wood. For Spanish, Sam had to buy tortillas, cheese, black beans, lettuce, tomatoes, and sour cream. Sam knew her mom would be irritated because she would have to run all those errands. Sam had a soccer tournament and would not be able to help shop, so she decided to make an organized chart to help her mom pick up all the materials efficiently.

2. Today I am going to discuss digestion. Digestion is the process of breaking food down into a useable energy for the body. Digestion actually begins in the mouth when saliva is mixed with food as a person chews. A chewed ball of food is called a *bolus*. The bolus travels from the mouth to the pharynx and into the esophagus. The bolus is moved down into the stomach through the esophagus through a passive process called *peristalsis*. The esophagus actually contracts in waves, moving the food down. When the bolus passes through the lower esophageal sphincter, it goes into the stomach.

3. To title an assignment properly, in the upper right corner, please write your first and last name. Under your name, write the class and period. Under the name of the class, write the date. In the upper left corner, be sure to include the title of the assignment. Now you are ready to begin the assignment. Pay attention to the margins and write legibly.

Identifying Key Concepts

▶ **Goal:** *The student will learn to remember information by selecting only the critical parts of material presented orally.*

Review the five key *wh-* words: *who, what, where, when,* and *why.* You might want to write them down for the student. As part of your review, you may also want to use the passages in the exercises to practice the *wh-* questions.

Read each sentence or passage in the exercises on pages 59-68 aloud and have the student identify the critical information you ask for. Encourage the student to draw diagrams or take notes as needed.

In Exercises 6-10, there may be more than one answer to the *wh-* questions. As the student answers the questions, have him first identify the main answer to each question. For additional practice, have the student identify other possible answers to the *wh-* questions.

Note: Answers to the questions are italicized.

Exercise 1

▶ **Goal:** *The student will learn to remember information by selecting only the critical parts of material presented orally.*

Remind the student to listen for the *wh-* word. Then read each sentence aloud and have the student identify the critical information you ask for.

1. Listen and identify **who**.

   George Washington was the only president to be elected unanimously.

2. Listen and identify **what**.

   George Washington was the *first president of the United States*.

3. Listen and identify **where**.

   George Washington is buried in *Mount Vernon*.

4. Listen and identify **when**.

   George Washington was president from *1789 to 1797*.

Exercise 2

▶ **Goal:** *The student will learn to remember information by selecting only the critical parts of material presented orally.*

Remind the student to listen for the *wh-* word. Then read each passage aloud and have the student identify the critical information you ask for.

1. Listen and identify **who**.

    Jorge and Brian walked to the mall to buy a new video game. On the way, it started to rain so they decided to go to the movies instead.

2. Listen and identify **what**.

    Sarah went to the store to buy *milk, bread, and apples*.

3. Listen and identify **where**.

    Carolyn and Anne live in *Denver*. They like to ski and go shopping on the weekends.

4. Listen and identify **when**.

    On *Saturday*, Mrs. Smith threw a party for her class. Everyone was invited to the park for lunch and games.

Exercise 3

▶ **Goal:** *The student will learn to remember information by selecting only the critical parts of material presented orally.*

Remind the student to listen for the *wh-* words. Then read each passage aloud and have the student identify the critical information you ask for.

1. Listen and identify ***where*** and ***what***.

   Thomas Jefferson was *governor of the state of Virginia* from 1779-1781 before becoming president.

2. Listen and identify ***who*** and ***when***.

   Alexander Hamilton was important in Thomas Jefferson's presidential win in *1800*.

3. Listen and identify ***who*** and ***where***.

   Thomas Jefferson attended the *College of William and Mary in Virginia* in 1760.

4. Listen and identify ***what*** and ***when***.

   Thomas Jefferson acted as *vice president* for John Adams from *1797-1801*.

Exercise 4

▶ **Goal:** *The student will learn to remember information by selecting only the critical parts of material presented orally.*

Remind the student to listen for the *wh-* words. Then read each passage aloud and have the student identify the critical information you ask for.

1. Listen and identify **who** and **what**.

   Theodore Roosevelt was the *26th president* of the United States of America. He was president for two terms and was a *member of the Republican party*.

2. Listen and identify **what** and **where**.

   Theodore Roosevelt was *governor* of the state of *New York* from 1898-1900.

3. Listen and identify **when** and **where**.

   Theodore Roosevelt was born in *1858* to a socially prominent *New York* family. He was tutored *at home* until he went to *Harvard University*.

4. Listen and identify **who** and **when**.

   In *1903*, a stuffed toy was given to *Teddy Roosevelt*. Based on one story, this gift led to the naming of "teddy" bears.

Exercise 5

▶ **Goal:** *The student will learn to remember information by selecting only the critical parts of material presented orally.*

Remind the student to listen for the *wh-* words. Then read each passage aloud and have the student identify the critical information you ask for.

1. Listen and identify **when** and **why**.

   Abraham Lincoln was the 16th president of the United States of America. He was president *during the Civil War*. The Civil War began as *a result of disagreements between citizens in the northern U.S. states and the southern U.S. states*.

2. Listen and identify **what** and **why**.

   President Lincoln believed in *keeping the United States as one* because *he felt that leaving the Union was illegal*. However, the states in the south wanted to separate from the northern states because of the slavery issue.

3. Listen and identify **who** and **why**.

   Abraham Lincoln issued the Emancipation Proclamation on January 1, 1863 in Washington. This proclamation was issued *to declare forever free the slaves within the Confederate states*.

4. Listen and identify **where** and **why**.

   On April 14, 1865, Abraham Lincoln was assassinated at *Ford's Theatre in Washington* by John Wilkes Booth, an actor. *Booth believed he was helping the south by killing President Lincoln*. Lincoln was the first president to be assassinated.

Exercise 6

> **Goal:** *The student will learn to remember information by selecting only the critical parts of material presented orally.*

Remind the student to listen for the *wh-* words. Then read each passage aloud and have the student identify the critical information you ask for.

1. Listen and identify **who** and **what**.

   Mr. Mayer found big, *dirty footprints in the kitchen*. He sighed loudly because he had just finished mopping the floors. "*Charlie!*" he yelled, "Please come here immediately!" Charlie rounded the corner and stomped into the kitchen wearing dirty boots. He stopped abruptly when he caught a glimpse of his father's face and the dirty floor. "Sorry," he muttered with his head down.

2. Listen and identify **what** and **where**.

   The pilot prepared to fly *the plane* from *Chicago to Los Angeles*. Drinks and a snack would be served. As the pilot watched the passengers board the plane, he noticed that many of them were excited.

3. Listen and identify **where** and **when**.

   The *Oklahoma* State Fair is located at *State Fair Park* and runs in *September*. Fair Day in Oklahoma is usually the *third Monday in September*. Fair Day is Brenda's favorite day. School is dismissed at *1:00 p.m.* Brenda immediately meets her three best friends in the *courtyard at school* as soon as school lets out. Her mom always drives the girls to *the fair* and drops them off at the *main gate* at *2:00 p.m.* The girls ride the rides, eat hamburgers and fries, and listen to music. They all have fun.

4. Listen and identify **where** and **when**.

   Some birds fly *south* in the *early winter*. This is called "migrating." The birds move, or migrate, south for warmer weather. In the *spring*, the birds return to the *north*. Some people also migrate or move seasonally to avoid cold weather. These migrating people are sometimes called "snowbirds."

Exercise 7

▶ **Goal:** *The student will learn to remember information by selecting only the critical parts of material presented orally.*

Remind the student to listen for the *wh-* words. Then read each passage aloud and have the student identify the critical information you ask for.

1. Listen and identify **who** and **what**.

   Jeremy needed to get *his father* a *birthday gift*. Unfortunately, Jeremy only had a few dollars left of his allowance and he knew it wasn't enough for a nice gift. Luckily, Jeremy was creative. He was taking woodworking at school so Jeremy decided to make a *photo frame*. When Jeremy was finished, the frame was beautiful. Jeremy's dad loved it.

2. Listen and identify **who** and **when**.

   Yesterday, *Julia* stayed home from school because she had a fever. She felt horrible! Julia thought she would be able to get comfortable in the family room and watch TV. The thought of watching TV all day made her feel a little better. However, *Julia's mom* had other ideas. She made Julia stay in her room *all day* with no TV or phone. All she could do was read. The *next day*, Julia went back to school.

3. Listen and identify **what** and **where**.

   Seven sixth graders were awarded *citizenship awards* at a ceremony in the *school auditorium*. Not only did the students *pick up litter around the school*, they also *helped tutor their peers* after school in *the library*. The teachers and principal were so impressed with the students' efforts, they created a special award to give to each student. Even more students want to help out around the school next year.

4. Listen and identify **where** and **when**.

   Mr. McGee escaped from his *yard* on *Saturday* while his owners were at the grocery store. The little dog had discovered a small hole near the fence and quickly got busy digging. Shortly, that little hole was big enough for Mr. McGee to slip through. He took a walk to the *park* and then went to visit his friend, Barley, who lived *next door*. When he got home and scratched at the door, his owners ran to let him in. First he got lots of loves and then he got lots of angry looks. The owners filled in the hole under the fence right away. No more escapes for Mr. McGee!

Exercise 8

▶ **Goal:** *The student will learn to remember information by selecting only the critical parts of material presented orally.*

Remind the student to listen for the *wh-* words. Then read each passage aloud and have the student identify the critical information you ask for.

1. Listen and identify **what** and **when**.

   Ms. Cheng and her third-grade class *dressed up in costume and performed a dance* for the rest of the school *last Wednesday* to celebrate the Chinese New Year.

2. Listen and identify **who** and **what**.

   Over the summer, the *sixth-grade students* at Learner Middle School were *required to read two books*. *Mia* figured out that she would have to *read a total of 400 pages* between the two books to finish before the school year began. She only wanted to read on weekdays. Mia had 10 weeks to finish both books. She calculated that she had to *read eight pages per night*.

3. Listen and identify **who**, **what**, and **when**.

   Trevor, a seventh-grade student, spent four days *preparing for his social studies test* he would take on *Friday*. On *Monday*, he reviewed past quizzes. On *Tuesday*, he made vocabulary flash cards. On *Wednesday*, Trevor completed the review sheet that was handed out in class. On *Thursday*, he reviewed all of his materials again, and had his best friend, *Tony*, quiz him. Because of his hard work, Trevor received an A on his social studies test.

4. Listen and identify **who**, **what**, **where**, and **when**.

   Mrs. Johnson gave *the class* a *group assignment to create a newspaper*. The students were instructed to form groups of three and were given a month to complete the project. All work was to be done *in the classroom*. The newspaper needed to include school news, national news, sports updates, editorials, and comics.

Exercise 9

▶ **Goal:** *The student will learn to remember information by selecting only the critical parts of material presented orally.*

Remind the student to listen for the *wh-* words. Then read each passage aloud and have the student identify the critical information you ask for.

1. Listen and identify **who** and **what**.

   About one hundred years ago, British physicist *J.J. Thomson* began *looking inside the atom*. At the Cavendish Laboratory at Cambridge University, Thomson experimented with currents of electricity inside empty glass tubes. He *investigated a long-standing puzzle known as a "cathode ray."*

2. Listen and identify **what** and **when**.

   The *discoveries of early scientists* drastically changed the way people thought about our world *hundreds of years ago*. First, Galileo's discoveries about falling objects changed our perception of *time*. Newton described the dance of the *planets* as well as falling objects, and Einstein's equations expanded *the universe*. All of these men were leaders in science.

3. Listen and identify **what, where,** and **when**.

   Have you ever seen a *comet*? Comets are *chunks of ice and dust* that sometimes pass into the center of the solar system from *outer space*. Some comets travel in *elliptical paths that circle near the sun and then go out past Pluto*. When comets get close enough to the sun, heat makes them start to evaporate. Jets of gas and dust form long tails that we can see from Earth. These tails can sometimes be millions of miles long. *Halley's comet* circles by Earth *every 76 years* and was last seen in *1986*.

4. Listen and identify **why**.

   There are 206 bones in your body. They *offer support, leverage, and protection*. There are several layers in bone. The outer layer is a thin, dense membrane that nourishes the bone. The next layer is the part you see when you look at a skeleton. Inside this layer is a spongy layer. This layer is very strong. The innermost part of the bone is sort of like a thick jelly. Its job is to make blood cells.

Exercise 10

▶ **Goal:** *The student will learn to remember information by selecting only the critical parts of material presented orally.*

Remind the student to listen for the *wh-* word. Then read each passage aloud and have the student identify the critical information you ask for.

1. Listen and identify **why**.
   Hibernation is the way that animals adapt to the climate and land around them. Animals must be able to live through extreme cold or they will die. They hibernate, or sleep deeply, *in order to escape that cold*. They also hibernate because *it is extremely difficult to find food during the winter*. Badgers, bears, hedgehogs, chipmunks, and prairie dogs are animals that hibernate in the winter.

2. Listen and identify **why**.
   The United States Secret Service exists for two major reasons: *protection and criminal investigations*. Secret Service agents are responsible for protecting the president, vice-president, their families, heads of state, and other designated individuals. They also protect the White House and other buildings in Washington, D.C. Secret Service agents also investigate crimes that relate to stealing money, identities, and computer information.

3. Listen and identify **why**.
   Our senses—sight, hearing, smell, touch, and taste—are critical for everyday life. They *keep us safe, allow us to learn, and help us enjoy life*. However, not all the senses are necessary to get the most out of life. For example, canes and seeing-eye dogs can help people who are blind stay safe while walking around. Sign language can help students who are hard-of-hearing communicate and learn. If one of the senses does not work properly, the others often become stronger, or more acute. Senses are important to humans.

4. Listen and identify **why**.
   Sneezing is *the body's response to irritations in the nose*. First chemicals are released in the lining of the nose. These chemicals are released when the body is exposed to viral infections, allergens, or physical irritants like smoke, pollution, perfumes, and cold air. When these chemicals are released, the nerve endings in the mucous lining of the nose are stimulated. Nerve stimulation leads to the activation of a reflex in the brain. The reflex sends messages to the muscles in the head and neck. Air pressure builds up in the lungs because the vocal folds, or chords, stay closed. The sudden opening of the vocal folds forces the air out through the nose and mouth helping to expel the irritants from the body.

Linking & Associations

▶ **Goal:** *The student will learn to remember auditory information by tying material together.*

Give each student paper and a pen or pencil. Use the following examples to show the student how to link words together using a drawing or a sentence.

Have the student complete the exercises on pages 70-79. Read each word list aloud. First have the student draw a sketch that incorporates all of the words in the list. This should be a very simple drawing that links the words together in a real or silly way. Then have the student describe the drawing, using the words to create a sentence. Repeat each list as needed.

Note: The words in the exercises have been divided into two categories: related and unrelated.

Example 1 (related):
book, paper, eraser, desk

Sentence (real):
The book, paper, and eraser were on the desk.

Example 2 (unrelated):
bee, flag, ring, flower, chair

Sentence (silly):
The bee looked for the ring by the flag, by the flower, and on the chair.

Exercise *1*

▶ **Goal:** *The student will learn to remember auditory information by tying material together.*

Read each word list aloud. Have the student draw a picture that incorporates all of the words. The simple drawing should link the words together in a real or silly way. Then have the student use the words to describe the drawing.

Related Words

1. boy, shirt, sock, sweater, jeans

2. sand, towel, water, pail, umbrella

3. table, hamburger, French fries, soda, sundae

4. barn, chicken, sheep, cow, hay

5. sun, cloud, rain, snow, wind

Unrelated Words

1. cup, shoe, pen, paper clip, honey

2. crocodile, pudding, plant, fly, sock

3. nose, car, grape, carpet, bed

4. house, bus, basketball, television, worm

5. girl, lemon, door, telephone, sink

Exercise 2

▶ **Goal:** *The student will learn to remember auditory information by tying material together.*

Read each word list aloud. Have the student draw a picture that incorporates all of the words. The simple drawing should link the words together in a real or silly way. Then have the student use the words to describe the drawing.

Related Words

1. pool, water, diving board, ladder, stairs, lifeguard

2. picnic bench, swing set, tree, sandbox, grass, slide

3. toothbrush, toothpaste, floss, hair dryer, towel, comb

4. stadium, home plate, ball, bat, hot dog, peanuts

5. test, notebook, book, study, desk, night

Unrelated Words

1. clock, run, fast, candy, candle, bathtub

2. dessert, ship, stripe, crayon, lunch, thumb

3. restaurant, bathroom, hairbrush, backpack, horse, jump rope

4. saw, carpet, hallway, finger, radio, shout

5. strawberry, money, hose, salt, ring, basket

Exercise 3

▶ **Goal:** *The student will learn to remember auditory information by tying material together.*

Read each word list aloud. Have the student draw a picture that incorporates all of the words. The simple drawing should link the words together in a real or silly way. Then have the student use the words to describe the drawing.

Related Words

1. rides, Ferris wheel, roller coaster, cotton candy, log ride, lazy river, bumper cars

2. airplane, family, suitcases, hotel, rental car, camera, map

3. drive, car, door, seat, oil, gas, seat belt

4. race, number, shorts, tank top, running shoes, hat, sunscreen

5. visit, monkeys, zookeeper, elephants, walk, watch, feed

Unrelated Words

1. stomach, game, funny, teacher, canoe, sing, pitcher

2. back, eat, fly, wheel, notebook, carrot, nail

3. zebra, museum, race, eyebrow, ticket, airplane, book

4. sleep, wall, mix, belt, sunglasses, tie, yellow

5. tomato, classroom, smile, P.E., crib, shade, shampoo

Exercise *4*

▶ **Goal:** *The student will learn to remember auditory information by tying material together.*

Read each word list aloud. Have the student draw a picture that incorporates all of the words. The simple drawing should link the words together in a real or silly way. Then have the student use the words to describe the drawing.

Related Words

1. Hollywood, actor, California, sunglasses, award, wealthy, movie, TV show

2. treadmill, weights, jump rope, mat, water, trainer, stretch, breathe

3. desk, office, manager, suit, lunch, break, telephone, computer

4. read, TV, friends, movie, dinner, party, sleep, concert

5. compass, backpack, mountain, trail, lost, view, jacket, climb

Unrelated Words

1. foot, sore, lotion, stove, stop, garbage can, pen, sun

2. store, write, tray, sign, vase, bird, thermometer, apple

3. bread, gas, square, soap, think, break, talk, word

4. cry, long, curl, jacket, pillow, grow, turkey, twist

5. tape, pumpkin, light, moon, aqua, wave, knob, earring

Exercise 5

▶ **Goal:** *The student will learn to remember auditory information by tying material together.*

Read each word list aloud. Have the student draw a picture that incorporates all of the words. The simple drawing should link the words together in a real or silly way. Then have the student use the words to describe the drawing.

Related Words

1. barbecue, tongs, heat, cook, chicken, steak, vegetables

2. lawn, garden, yard, flowers, hose, soil, seeds

3. tacos, burritos, rice, beans, tortillas, salsa, cheese

4. carpet, tile, hardwood, rug, stone, brick, dirt

5. hike, bike, run, ski, snowboard, canoe, camp

Unrelated Words

1. stool, bag, cat, key, thumb, window, leaf

2. sand, heel, tape, starfish, tie, bread, strap

3. dial, cart, five, weather, satellite, shoulder, balloon

4. wheelchair, ring, race, raccoon, plant, shirt, oven

5. boat, sprinkler, factory, valley, goal, city, summer

Exercise 6

▶ **Goal:** *The student will learn to remember auditory information by tying material together.*

Read each word list aloud. Have the student draw a picture that incorporates all of the words. The simple drawing should link the words together in a real or silly way. Then have the student use the words to describe the drawing.

Related Words

1. feature, editorial, comics, sports, ads, local, TV guide, fashion

2. chimney, paint, bathroom, build, fix, hinge, counter, tile

3. mall, bag, food court, register, sales clerk, dressing room, sales, purchase

4. disappointed, happy, sad, surprised, angry, depressed, tired, excited

5. green, flag, club, hole, ball, concentrate, wait, practice

Unrelated Words

1. mango, round, serious, math, lemon, sting, bandage, read

2. clap, leaf, straight, smile, grow, hit, salt, school

3. fan, pound, story, paragraph, newspaper, line, eyelash, blank

4. spider, dream, bite, home, fortune, sink, directions, bank

5. tornado, homework, attack, fence, water, interview, wire, vote

Exercise 7

▶ **Goal:** *The student will learn to remember auditory information by tying material together.*

Read each word list aloud. Have the student draw a picture that incorporates all of the words. The simple drawing should link the words together in a real or silly way. Then have the student use the words to describe the drawing.

Related Words

1. check-out line, select, shop, cart, list, produce, deli, bakery

2. traffic, freeway, ride, drive, bus, carpool, stop sign, taxi

3. camp, work, library, play, swim, sun, warm, relax

4. mitt, cleats, bases, bat, umpire, players, bench, coach

5. paper, paints, chalk, markers, scissors, glue, decorate, stencils

Unrelated Words

1. submarine, hurricane, danger, soldier, poison, duck, divide, planet

2. alarm clock, spaceship, destroy, fingernail, barbecue, pelican, ham, red

3. curtain, city, exit, billboard, fruit, transportation, jam, soft

4. rectangle, sharp, age, weak, ear, problem, conclusion, sister

5. cushion, heater, move, flood, crackle, marshmallow, sentence, principal

Exercise 8

▶ **Goal:** *The student will learn to remember auditory information by tying material together.*

Read each word list aloud. Have the student draw a picture that incorporates all of the words. The simple drawing should link the words together in a real or silly way. Then have the student use the words to describe the drawing.

Related Words

1. physician, nurse, writer, teacher, construction worker, firefighter, pilot, actress

2. cook, waiter, serve, course, menu, order, bill, pay

3. fiction, nonfiction, mystery, romance, drama, science fiction, comedy, biography

4. period, comma, colon, semicolon, dash, question mark, exclamation mark, quotation marks

5. Union, Confederacy, musket, soldier, Lincoln, combat, freedom, North

Unrelated Words

1. money, spinach, price, vacant, family, full, month, apartment

2. science, calendar, soap, dirty, booth, warm, stomach, salad

3. hungry, loaf, broil, grill, straw, February, blink, ornament

4. tap, diamond, shake, sliver, cheesecake, camera, mural, bridge

5. bone, counter, figure, multiply, germ, novel, fight, dishcloth

Exercise *9*

▶ **Goal:** *The student will learn to remember auditory information by tying material together.*

Read each word list aloud. Have the student draw a picture that incorporates all of the words. The simple drawing should link the words together in a real or silly way. Then have the student use the words to describe the drawing.

Related Words

1. observe, data, biology, notebook, zoology, botany, glass, microscope

2. chemistry, test tube, goggles, atom, molecule, burner, biochemistry, electron

3. cell, nucleus, plasma, divide, multiply, cytoplasm, membrane, osmosis

4. government, constitution, amendment, citizens, legislature, delegates, boycott, vote

5. North Pole, South Pole, latitude, longitude, equator, Earth, globe, continent

Unrelated Words

1. oyster, train, alone, storm, lounge, surprise, temporary, chain

2. leave, cheap, vegetarian, library, canal, hunger, factory, tunnel

3. garage, gold, comfort, new, dive, apartment, view, cube

4. bump, travel, onion, police, toxic, share, location, line

5. money, drive, remove, follow, island, stream, rent, zipper

Exercise 10

▶ **Goal:** *The student will learn to remember auditory information by tying material together.*

Read each word list aloud. Have the student draw a picture that incorporates all of the words. The simple drawing should link the words together in a real or silly way. Then have the student use the words to describe the drawing.

Related Words

1. angle, vertex, protractor, acute, obtuse, right

2. line, endpoint, intersection, parallel, perpendicular, rays

3. radius, diameter, circle, circumference, pi, compass

4. triangle, measure, perimeter, area, rectangle, trapezoid

5. multiplication, division, algebra, square, cube, root

Unrelated Words

1. advice, tantrum, question, end, payment, empty

2. weird, world, Jupiter, travel, breathe, give

3. partner, chores, exercise, dispute, anything, response

4. challenge, brilliant, concerned, careful, freeze, vision

5. freedom, switch, current, allow, improve, wrap

Visualizing

▶ **Goal:** *The student will learn to remember auditory information by using more than one modality.*

Have the student create a mental picture, real or silly, of the word, sentence, or paragraph in the exercises on pages 81-90. After the student has created his picture, have him describe in detail what he is picturing.

To help students with this task, have the student draw the picture on paper and then explain it. Eliminate the drawing as soon as the student is able to describe the picture in his mind without the visual cue. The words below can also be used as cues to help students remember what they have heard.

Cue Words		
who	color	texture
what	size	mood
where	shape	movement
when	number	sound

There are three sections in each exercise.

Words

Sentences
In Exercises 6-10, the sentences build upon one another to make up a paragraph. Once the student has completed all of the sentences in the section, you may want to have him recall the entire set of sentences.

Paragraphs
For additional practice with paragraphs, pull paragraphs out of textbooks or novels being read in the student's classroom. Expand to multiple paragraphs.

Exercise 1

▶ **Goal:** *The student will learn to remember auditory information by using more than one modality.*

Read each word, sentence, or paragraph aloud to the student. Have the student create a picture in his mind of the word, sentence, or paragraph. Then have the student describe in detail what he is picturing.

Words

1. shoe
2. apple
3. dog
4. girl
5. bus

Sentences

1. Sam tied his shoe.
2. Callie ate an apple.
3. The dog jumped up.
4. The girl was happy.
5. The bus was yellow.

Paragraph

1. Sam ran outside to play with his friend Joe. On his way to Joe's house, Sam realized that one of his shoelaces wasn't tied. Sam tied his shoe.

2. Callie's mom returned from the grocery store with two large bags of groceries. Starving, Callie reached into one of the bags and ate an apple.

3. The large dog jumped in the air to fetch a Frisbee.

4. The girl, who was eating the chocolate birthday cake, smiled.

5. The big, yellow bus dropped the students off in front of the school.

Exercise 2

▶ **Goal:** *The student will learn to remember auditory information by using more than one modality.*

Read each word, sentence, or paragraph aloud to the student. Have the student create a picture in his mind of the word, sentence, or paragraph. Then have the student describe in detail what he is picturing.

Words

1. flower
2. book
3. computer
4. car
5. candle

Sentences

1. The girl picked a flower from the garden.
2. The boy read the book.
3. The computer is on the desk.
4. The car is parked in the driveway.
5. The woman lit the candle.

Paragraphs

1. On a beautiful Sunday morning, the young girl went outside and picked a flower from the garden.
2. During recess, the boy read his book under a shady tree.
3. The teenage boy turned on the laptop computer that was on his desk.
4. The woman's car is parked in the driveway next to the gas station.
5. The woman lit the candle on the table before serving dinner.

Exercise 3

▶ **Goal:** *The student will learn to remember auditory information by using more than one modality.*

Read each word, sentence, or paragraph aloud to the student. Have the student create a picture in his mind of the word, sentence, or paragraph. Then have the student describe in detail what he is picturing.

Words

1. chocolate cake
2. tennis shoes
3. yellow flower
4. green grass
5. red carpet

Sentences

1. The boy devoured the piece of chocolate cake that was left over from his birthday party.
2. The tall girl tied her tennis shoes before going outside.
3. The woman picked the yellow flower out of her garden.
4. The tall, green grass surrounded the red, brick home.
5. She chose red carpet to go in the dining room.

Paragraphs

1. It was Charlie's 10th birthday party. After the guests left his party, Charlie devoured the last piece of chocolate cake.
2. Serena had longed to play outside as it was the first day of spring. The tall girl tied her tennis shoes and ran out the door.
3. At the beginning of spring, Mary had planted flower seeds in her garden. Two months later, she picked the yellow flowers that had finally bloomed.
4. The tall, green grass surrounded the red, brick home of the Smith family.
5. Wanting to add more color to her home, Kelly chose red carpet to go in the dining room.

Exercise 4

▶ **Goal:** *The student will learn to remember auditory information by using more than one modality.*

Read each word, sentence, or paragraph aloud to the student. Have the student create a picture in his mind of the word, sentence, or paragraph. Then have the student describe in detail what he is picturing.

Words

1. walking
2. writing
3. floating
4. swimming
5. listening

Sentences

1. The boy was walking through the park when it started to rain.
2. The fourth graders were required to do ten writing assignments during the year.
3. Suddenly a seal jumped over the log that was floating in the ocean.
4. Karen participated in a triathlon that involved running, swimming, and biking.
5. Listening to music is Rafael's favorite after-school activity.

Paragraphs

1. The young boy was walking through his neighborhood park. Suddenly, the sky turned ominously dark and it started to rain.
2. The fourth graders were required to do ten writing assignments during the year. Five needed to be book summaries and five needed to be descriptive writings.
3. A log was floating in the ocean. Suddenly a seal jumped out of the water and over the log.
4. Karen participated in a triathlon that involved six miles of running, one mile of swimming, and 15 miles of biking. Karen was exhausted when she finished.
5. Listening to music is Rafael's favorite after-school activity. When he gets home from school, Rafael lies down on his bed and turns on the radio.

Exercise 5

▶ **Goal:** *The student will learn to remember auditory information by using more than one modality.*

Read each word, sentence, or paragraph aloud to the student. Have the student create a picture in his mind of the word, sentence, or paragraph. Then have the student describe in detail what he is picturing.

Words

1. loneliness
2. joy
3. sadness
4. famous
5. humorous

Sentences

1. The girl's loneliness increased after her puppy died.
2. It was a joy to watch the children play.
3. Sadness filled the room when the students heard about the devastating hurricane.
4. When she won the award, Selena felt like she was famous.
5. The television show was humorous.

Paragraphs

1. The girl's loneliness increased after her puppy died. She sat in her room alone for several days after he was gone.
2. The Adams Elementary PTA raised money for a new play structure for the playground. It was a joy to watch the children play on it.
3. The students watched the news report detailing a Class 5 hurricane hitting the Gulf Coast. Upon seeing the news report, sadness filled the room.
4. Selena won an award for writing the winning state-wide essay on the history of her school. When she won the award, she felt like she was famous.
5. Kate watched her favorite television program on Thursday night. It was her favorite show because it was humorous and made her laugh.

Exercise 6

▶ **Goal:** *The student will learn to remember auditory information by using more than one modality.*

Read each word, sentence, or paragraph aloud to the student. Have the student create a picture in his mind of the word, sentence, or paragraph. Then have the student describe in detail what he is picturing.

Words

1. yogurt
2. mouse
3. bank
4. ride
5. add

Sentences

1. Last night, Thomas had a birthday party.
2. Thomas sent invitations that looked like basketballs to seven of his best friends.
3. All the boys were able to come, and they showed up at Thomas's house at 5 o'clock.
4. First all eight children played basketball. Then Thomas opened his gifts.
5. Thomas was sad when the party ended.

Paragraph

Yesterday my fourth-grade class went to the zoo. First we saw the monkeys. They were chasing each other around the trees while making loud screeching noises. Then we saw the elephants and giraffes but they were boring. All they did was stand there and chew on nothing. The tigers were more interesting, though. They paced around their habitat and roared at us.

Exercise 7

▶ **Goal:** *The student will learn to remember auditory information by using more than one modality.*

Read each word, sentence, or paragraph aloud to the student. Have the student create a picture in his mind of the word, sentence, or paragraph. Then have the student describe in detail what he is picturing.

Words

1. run
2. equal
3. draw
4. learn
5. jealous

Sentences

1. Yesterday the swim team held a car wash.
2. The gas station on the corner of Bridgeport and 40th let the team use their parking lot.
3. Everybody wore the school colors, blue and white, and the car wash was busy from 8 a.m. to 5 p.m.
4. All of the money raised helped buy suits, caps, and goggles for the swimmers.
5. The girls not only raised enough money for all the swim gear, but they had fun doing it!

Paragraph

Jack loves to watch TV. On Saturdays, he gets up at 6 a.m. to watch cartoons before his soccer game. On weekdays, he watches his favorite shows while he eats his breakfast. Then when he gets home from school, he does his homework in front of the TV. However, yesterday, Jack's mom got his grades. They were not very good, so Jack has to study on Saturday mornings and read during breakfast instead of watch TV.

Exercise 8

▶ **Goal:** *The student will learn to remember auditory information by using more than one modality.*

Read each word, sentence, or paragraph aloud to the student. Have the student create a picture in his mind of the word, sentence, or paragraph. Then have the student describe in detail what he is picturing.

Words

1. platter
2. breakfast
3. envy
4. joke
5. finish

Sentences

1. The Vikings had a big game last Friday.
2. The stands filled up early and everyone cheered loudly when the team was announced.
3. The home team scored first when the quarterback threw the ball to a wide end for a touchdown.
4. At halftime, the score was tied.
5. Neither team scored again until the last minute of the fourth quarter when the Vikings kicked the winning field goal.

Paragraph

Ian had a scary accident last weekend. He went snowboarding with his friend Claire. Halfway down the first run, Ian fell and couldn't get up. Claire continued down the run to the ski patrol to get help. The ski patrol used a sled to get Ian down to the first-aid station. Ian ended up with a broken collarbone and many sore muscles but otherwise he was okay. He will always wear a helmet and be more careful from now on when he goes snowboarding.

Exercise 9

▶ **Goal:** *The student will learn to remember auditory information by using more than one modality.*

Read each word, sentence, or paragraph aloud to the student. Have the student create a picture in his mind of the word, sentence, or paragraph. Then have the student describe in detail what he is picturing.

Words

1. many
2. river
3. skip
4. excited
5. win

Sentences

1. Elephants live in Africa and Asia.
2. The African elephant is larger than the Asian elephant.
3. Elephants are believed to have good memories.
4. Over 50 years ago, many elephants in one herd were killed by poachers, or people who hunt illegally.
5. After so many elephants in the herd were killed, the other elephants in the herd avoided the area.

Paragraph

American pioneers traveled across the continent in adverse conditions. They faced violence, hunger, thirst, hypothermia, heat stroke, and more. One account of the great trek was told from the perspective of a doll. The book, *Patty Reed's Doll*, shares the story of a little girl, Patty, who travels to California with her family and her doll. The group runs into all sorts of problems, including heavy early snows in the Sierra Mountains. Read more to find out how the novel ends.

Exercise *10*

▶ **Goal:** *The student will learn to remember auditory information by using more than one modality.*

Read each word, sentence, or paragraph aloud to the student. Have the student create a picture in his mind of the word, sentence, or paragraph. Then have the student describe in detail what he is picturing.

Words

1. third
2. and
3. also
4. however
5. but

Sentences

1. In math class today, we learned about the order of operations.
2. The teacher wrote a weird word on the board: PEMDAS.
3. He said that each letter stands for a math operation and that we are supposed to do each operation in the order that the letters come in the word PEMDAS.
4. First I look for any parenthesis (P) and do them, then I do exponents (E), and then I do multiplication (M).
5. After multiplication comes D for division, A for addition, and finally, S for subtraction.

Paragraph

Segregation means separating people. Segregation was once a big problem in parts of the United States of America. Black Americans were not allowed the same rights as the whites. They unfairly had to drink out of designated drinking fountains, attend black schools, and even ride in the back of busses if white Americans wanted the front seats. One woman, Rosa Parks, stood up for her rights as an American when she refused to move to the back of a bus. This action by Mrs. Parks helped ignite the fight for equal rights for all Americans.

Paraphrasing

▶ **Goal:** *The student will learn to remember information presented orally by processing, comprehending, and paraphrasing material in her own words.*

Use the following examples to show the student how to paraphrase, or restate, words, a set of directions, or a paragraph.

Have the student listen to each word, set of directions, or paragraph in the exercises on pages 92-101. If the student is working at the word level, have him name a synonym for each word. If the student is working at the following directions or paragraph level, have him paraphrase the directions or paragraph in his own words.

Words

1. seat chair

2. see look, view, stare, gaze

Following Directions

1. Press the ON button. Wait for the screen to light up and look for the icons to pop up. Then click on the program you want to use.

   Press the ON button. After the screen lights up and the icons pop up,

   click on the program you want to use.

Paragraph

Tyra went to the store with her mom to buy school supplies. She had a list of items she needed for school. The list included a notebook, pencils, and paper. For art, she needed markers and scissors. Tyra also needed to bring a roll of paper towels and a box of tissues for the class.

   Tyra got a notebook, pencils, paper, markers, and scissors. She also got

   paper towels and a box of tissues.

Exercise 1

▶ **Goal:** *The student will learn to remember information presented orally by processing, comprehending, and paraphrasing material in her own words.*

Ask the student to give a synonym for the words or paraphrase the directions and paragraphs in her own words.

Words

1. happy
2. sad
3. confused
4. road
5. under

Following Directions

1. Go to the store and buy some milk.
2. Take out your math book and open to page 23.
3. Draw a picture of a house, then draw a tree in front of the house.
4. Read the first chapter in your book and write a summary.
5. Study pages 40-60 in your math book for the math test.

Paragraph

On Sunday, Luis's mom began preparing for his birthday party. She went to the store and bought party hats, party favors, and balloons.

Exercise 2

▶ **Goal:** *The student will learn to remember information presented orally by processing, comprehending, and paraphrasing material in her own words.*

Ask the student to give a synonym for the words or paraphrase the directions and paragraphs in her own words.

Words

1. funny
2. walk
3. shut
4. thick
5. thin

Following Directions

1. To get to the zoo, take a right at the stop sign, then a left at the light.
2. Take out your science notebook and draw a picture of the solar system.
3. Take out the garbage, do the dishes, and sweep the floor.
4. Read a biography of a president, then write a two-paragraph summary.
5. Do problems 10-20 in your math journal but make sure you show all your work or you will not receive credit.

Paragraph

Jenna came home from school crying. Her mother noticed that Jenna's hair and clothes were soaked and her shoes were muddy. Jenna was shivering.

Exercise 3

▶ **Goal:** *The student will learn to remember information presented orally by processing, comprehending, and paraphrasing material in her own words.*

Ask the student to give a synonym for the words or paraphrase the directions and paragraphs in her own words.

Words

1. chair

2. sofa

3. pretty

4. disgusting

5. cup

Following Directions

1. Your teacher said, "Read to the end of the page, then close your book to indicate you have finished reading."

2. Your teacher said, "Do problems 20-40 on page 23 of your math book. Record your answers on a separate sheet of paper."

3. Your teacher said, "For our social studies test today, I want you to take a blank sheet of paper and write as much as you can about our unit on California."

4. Your teacher said, "After the bell rings, please push in your chairs and line up quietly at the door."

5. Your teacher said, "For our field trip tomorrow, please bring your own lunch because lunch will not be provided."

Paragraph

In the spring, baseball begins. Many people travel to Arizona to watch their favorite professional players prepare for the upcoming season. Fans are able to view practices and pre-season games.

Exercise 4

▶ **Goal:** *The student will learn to remember information presented orally by processing, comprehending, and paraphrasing material in her own words.*

Ask the student to give a synonym for the words or paraphrase the directions and paragraphs in her own words.

Words

1. helper
2. pest
3. dirty
4. teacher
5. tasty

Following Directions

1. Take out your French workbook. Do exercises 1-13 on page 24 and 1-5 on page 25.
2. When you are at the Farmer's Market, please buy spinach, two cucumbers, and a basket of strawberries.
3. Your chores this week include vacuuming the hardwood floors, taking out the trash, setting the table, and making your bed.
4. For your report on South Africa, please include information on climate, industry, population, and daily life.
5. When you make instant macaroni and cheese, boil the water first, then add the noodles. After the noodles are cooked, add the milk, cheese, and butter and mix together.

Paragraph

Today at lunch, Luke discovered the kitchen can be a dangerous place. He was boiling water to make macaroni and cheese. As the water was boiling, Luke got out a hot pad so he wouldn't burn his hand on the steam when he drained the macaroni. Unfortunately, he put the hot pad too close to the burner and it quickly caught fire. Luckily, Luke knew to yell for help. His grandmother came running down the stairs, grabbed the fire extinguisher from the closet, and put out the fire.

Exercise 5

▶ **Goal:** *The student will learn to remember information presented orally by processing, comprehending, and paraphrasing material in her own words.*

Ask the student to give a synonym for the words or paraphrase the directions and paragraphs in her own words.

Words

1. cut
2. caring
3. offer
4. sleep
5. gift

Following Directions

1. When you take a phone message, please write down the caller's first and last name, time he called, his phone number, and a brief message.

2. The fifth-grade teacher instructed his class to research a country in South America and write a two-page report about the country. Reports had to be typed and double spaced.

3. When you take out the garbage, make sure you tie the bag tightly, place it carefully in the garbage bin, and then wash your hands.

4. When washing white clothing, set the water temperature on warm, add bleach, add the clothes, and turn on the washing machine.

5. When going camping, remember to bring a tent, a sleeping bag, bug spray, and a flashlight.

Paragraph

Pedro helped his stepmother make pumpkin bread. After they mixed the ingredients together, Pedro's stepmother put the pumpkin bread in the oven for 45 minutes. When the buzzer rang, she took the bread out and let it cool for 10 minutes in the pan.

Exercise 6

▶ **Goal:** *The student will learn to remember information presented orally by processing, comprehending, and paraphrasing material in her own words.*

Ask the student to give a synonym for the words or paraphrase the directions and paragraphs in her own words.

Words

1. hurt
2. autumn
3. rug
4. house
5. father

Following Directions

1. Grab the knob, turn it, and pull toward you.
2. Pick up the round object, aim at the basket, and shoot.
3. Get out two slices of bread, spread peanut butter on one side of the bread and jam on the other, and put the two pieces of bread together.
4. Put paste on the brush, turn on the water and get the brush wet, then put it in your mouth.
5. Stop, get off, put down the kickstand, and take off your helmet.

Paragraph

The bell rang so the students looked at their teacher, Mrs. Snyder. As Mrs. Snyder dismissed them, she reminded the children to be back in line on time. Samuel picked up the red ball and James got the jump rope. Everyone headed outside into the sunshine.

Exercise 7

▶ **Goal:** *The student will learn to remember information presented orally by processing, comprehending, and paraphrasing material in her own words.*

Ask the student to give a synonym for the words or paraphrase the directions and paragraphs in her own words.

Words

1. hold
2. doze
3. complete
4. fragile
5. easy

Following Directions

1. Boil water in a pot; add pasta; drain the water; add cheese, milk, and butter.
2. Start with your feet together. Bend your knees, push yourself up off the ground, and then land back on the ground.
3. Put your face in the water and blow out, bring one arm out of the water and then the other, turn your head to the side, and take a breath.
4. Open the clip, hook it on the collar, open the door, and head outside.
5. Pick up the plates, glasses, and silverware. Walk into the kitchen, and put them by the sink.

Paragraph

Yesterday, my family got in the van and drove until we were in the mountains. Everyone was dressed in boots, shorts, and T-shirts. I carried a backpack full of water, snacks, and a sweatshirt in case the weather got cold. I felt really tired when I got to the top, but the view was spectacular. We had a great day.

Exercise 8

▶ **Goal:** *The student will learn to remember information presented orally by processing, comprehending, and paraphrasing material in her own words.*

Ask the student to give a synonym for the words or paraphrase the directions and paragraphs in her own words.

Words

1. shout
2. cry
3. shiver
4. slick
5. damp

Following Directions

1. Write your name and the date at the top and the numbers 1 through 20 down the side of your paper, then spell the word *similar* for number 1.
2. Open the bag, pour it into the bowl, and put the bowl down in front of the dog.
3. Point the remote, push the *ON* button, and select the channel you wish to watch.
4. Lie down on the ground, look up at the ceiling, put your hands behind your head, keep your elbows back, and slowly lift your upper body up, keeping your abdominal muscles tight.
5. Sit on the seat, pedal, and steer with the handlebars.

Paragraph

Julie and Jamal were hungry, so they pulled the dough out of the refrigerator and spread it on the pan. Then they spread sauce on the dough and sprinkled cheese and vegetables on top of the sauce. They slid the creation in the oven for 12 minutes until it was bubbly in the center and golden brown on the edges.

Exercise 9

> **Goal:** *The student will learn to remember information presented orally by processing, comprehending, and paraphrasing material in her own words.*

Ask the student to give a synonym for the words or paraphrase the directions and paragraphs in her own words.

Words

1. gathering
2. discover
3. grin
4. hard
5. limb

Following Directions

1. Turn on the faucet and place the glass beneath the stream.
2. Look at the notes, blow into the reed, and watch the conductor.
3. Press the power button, wait for it to boot up, click on a new document, and type three paragraphs.
4. Grab a towel and sunscreen, drive or walk to the water, and spread your towel on the sand.
5. Place two forks on the left side of the china, put a knife and a spoon to the right of the china, and place the water glass above the knife.

Paragraph

Stephanie and Andre got a group of people together at lunch. They asked Amy to write the feature article and Bijon to work on the sports. Stephanie knew that Rutger was a good artist, so she put him in charge of comics. Then Andre asked Paul to be in charge of editorials. Their first edition came out the following month. All of the kids had a great time.

Exercise 10

▶ **Goal:** *The student will learn to remember information presented orally by processing, comprehending, and paraphrasing material in her own words.*

Ask the student to give a synonym for the words or paraphrase the directions and paragraphs in her own words.

Words

1. demonstrate
2. destroy
3. rip
4. create
5. vanish

Following Directions

1. Get the can out of the freezer and let it thaw in the sink for 15-30 minutes. Open the can and place the contents in a pitcher. Add three full cans of water and stir.
2. Pull the bag out of the can, tie it tightly, open the door, walk outside, and put the bag in the trash can.
3. Place the tooth under your pillow, turn out the light, go to sleep, and check under the pillow in the morning.
4. Listen closely to the teacher. Raise your hand, wait to be called on, then speak.
5. Gather a piece of fruit, chips, and a granola bar, and make a peanut butter and jelly sandwich. Put all of the items in a bag.

Paragraph

Eliza peered into the tree where she heard the mewing. Big tears welled up in her eyes because she felt bad. Her dad wasn't home and her babysitter didn't know what to do. Eliza's neighbor called the fire department. The fire chief took pity on Eliza's situation and brought the truck with the tall ladder to Eliza's house. In minutes, the firefighters had brought the animal down from the top of the tree. Eliza hugged the cat and grinned from ear to ear.

Visual Memory Pretest/Posttest (Scoring)

Give the student pages 103 and 104. Have him read each item and then cover it with a sheet of paper. For items 2-5, allow him to take notes as needed. Then have the student repeat the information or answer the questions. For items 1-4, indicate each correct answer with the number **1**. For item 5, the student receives one point for each word or definition recalled correctly. An incorrect response receives a score of 0. Record the total number of correct answers at the bottom of this page to determine percentage correct.

Student Name: _____	Pretest Date	Posttest Date
1. a. 3511193 b. 4156881299 c. 412 North Bradley Road d. 12 South Bend Ave, Portland, OR 97219 e. malleus, incus, stapes f. parenthesis, exponents, multiplication, division, addition, subtraction	___ ___ ___ ___ ___ ___	___ ___ ___ ___ ___ ___
The student must recall five facts to mark this as correct. 2. The third-grade class at the Day School decided to host a fundraiser to raise money for a new gymnasium. They decided to organize a school-wide bake sale. The sixth graders sold $25 worth of baked goods, the third graders sold $50 worth of baked goods, and second graders sold $15 worth of baked goods. The kindergartners only raised $5 and all the other classrooms together raised $20. Did the bake sale raise over $100?	___	___
The student must recall eight facts to mark this as correct. 3. **Stella** **Niko** 11 years old 10 years old girl boy red hair brown hair green eyes brown eyes plays tennis plays tennis likes to read likes to read lives in New York lives in Athens, Greece	___	___
4. a. What has changed over the past 20 years? *school lunches* b. Why have schools changed school lunches? *to promote healthy eating habits*	___ ___	___ ___
The student receives one point for each word or definition recalled correctly (possible total of 10 points). If the student is having difficulty, present each item separately and have the student recall the information. Then see how many the student can remember as a group. 5. a. **admire** to look at something or someone with awe, respect, and honor b. **dictate** to say or read aloud c. **application** a form submitted to obtain an object or position; may or may not require approval d. **agoraphobia** an abnormal fear of public places with large numbers of people e. **zephyr** a slight breeze	___ (out of 10)	___ (out of 10)

Comments: _____

_____

	Pretest	Posttest
Number Correct	/20	/20
Percentage Correct	%	%

Visual Memory Pretest/Posttest

1. Look at each item below for five seconds. After looking at each one, cover it with a sheet of paper and repeat the information aloud.

   a. 3511193

   b. 4156881299

   c. 412 North Bradley Road

   d. 12 South Bend Ave, Portland, OR 97219

   e. invitation, cake, gift, birthday

   f. addition, subtraction, multiplication, division, parenthesis, exponents

2. Read the information and then cover the passage with a sheet of paper. Repeat the information aloud. Try to remember at least five facts. You may take notes as needed.

   The third-grade class at the Day School decided to host a fundraiser to raise money for a new gymnasium. They decided to organize a school-wide bake sale. The sixth graders sold $25 worth of baked goods, the third graders sold $50 worth of baked goods, and the second graders sold $15 worth of baked goods. The kindergartners only raised $5 and all the other classrooms together raised $20. Did the bake sale raise over $100?

3. Create a graph or chart to help you remember the following information. When your graph or chart is finished, study it. Then cover your graph or chart with a sheet of paper. Repeat at least eight facts aloud.

   Stella is an 11-year-old girl who lives in New York. She has red hair and green eyes. She plays tennis and likes to read.

   Niko is a 10-year-old boy who lives in Athens, Greece. He has brown hair and brown eyes. He plays tennis and likes to read.

4. Read the information and then cover the passage with a sheet of paper. Write your answers to the questions on the lines.

School lunches have changed over the past 20 years. Not only do schools charge more money for lunch, but many schools offer nutritious options. Students can now buy salads, fruits, and vegetables. Additionally, main dishes are often lower in fat and higher in nutritional value. Students are also educated about healthy eating habits. Hopefully, these changes will carry over into their adult lives.

a. What has changed over the past 20 years?

_____

b. Why have schools changed school lunches?

_____

5. Read and study all of the words and definitions listed below. Then cover the entire list and say the words and definitions aloud.

a. **admire**   to look at something or someone with awe, respect, and honor

b. **dictate**   to say or read aloud

c. **application**   a form submitted to obtain an object or position; may or may not require approval

d. **agoraphobia**   an abnormal fear of public places with large numbers of people

e. **zephyr**   a slight breeze

Strategies for Visual Memory

Acronyms & Silly Sentences: creating acronyms or silly sentences to remember written lists

    Goal: *The student will learn to remember written lists of related words.*

Chunking: dividing a large group of words, numbers, or items into smaller units

    Goal: *The student will learn to remember written information by breaking large groups of material into smaller, related units or categories.*

Defining & Drawing: writing definitions and sentences and creating drawings to reinforce vocabulary words

    Goal: *The student will learn to remember and recall vocabulary words using context clues and/or visual cues.*

Graphing & Charting: using visual graphs, charts, and diagrams to represent and organize information presented in written form

    Goal: *The student will learn to remember written information by using visual aids and organizers.*

Identifying Key Concepts: identifying the most important points of material presented in written form

    Goal: *The student will learn to remember information by selecting only the critical parts of written material.*

Paraphrasing: rewriting or restating written material

    Goal: *The student will learn to remember information presented in written form by processing, comprehending, and paraphrasing material in her own words.*

Saying, Tracing, Writing, & Drawing Sounds: saying, tracing, writing, and drawing phonemes in order to remember sounds and their corresponding written symbols

    Goal: *The student will learn to remember sounds and their corresponding written symbols.*

Visualizing: using mental pictures to represent material presented visually

    Goal: *The student will learn to remember written information by using more than one modality.*

Chunking

▶ **Goal:** *The student will learn to remember written information by breaking large groups of material into smaller, related units or categories.*

Show the student how to chunk a list of items into two (or more) groups based on category, pattern, or sequence. Visual cues can include the following:

- drawing lines or covering sections to break the numbers, words, or addresses into chunks

- looking for patterns (e.g., word/number patterns, area code/prefix/final digits)

- looking for items that have a personal association (e.g., age, birthday)

Have the student read each item and chunk the information in the exercises on pages 107-116. Then have him repeat each group, first with a visual cue and then without (e.g., cover the page or turn the page over). Have the student repeat the groups until he has memorized the item.

Remind the student that there may be more than one way to chunk the information.

Numbers

1. 6731655 = 673-1655 or 673/1655 or 67/316/55

2. 2062482368 = (206) 248-2368 or 206/248/2368 or 20/62/48/23/68

Addresses

1. 2638 West 78th Street = 2638/West 78th Street

2. 98123 65th Street, South City = 98123/65th Street/South City or
   98/123/65th Street/South City

Exercise 1

▶ **Goal:** *The student will learn to remember written information by breaking large groups of material into smaller, related units or categories.*

Read each item and chunk the information into two or more groups. Then repeat each group, first with a visual cue and then without. Repeat the groups until you have memorized the item.

Numbers

1. 8744424

2. 8911367

3. 8034258

4. 1813927

5. 1983063

Addresses

1. 224th Avenue SE

2. 432 Juniper Place NW

3. 487 Main Street

4. 310 Jefferson Way

5. 673 125th Drive

Exercise 2

▶ **Goal:** *The student will learn to remember written information by breaking large groups of material into smaller, related units or categories.*

Read each item and chunk the information into two or more groups. Then repeat each group, first with a visual cue and then without. Repeat the groups until you have memorized the item.

Numbers

1. 7849302

2. 0931763

3. 2340120

4. 8937654

5. 4538595

Addresses

1. 34 North Allen Street, Madison, WI

2. 112 Main Street, Chicago, IL

3. 78 Lombard Steet, San Francisco, CA

4. 99 West Fairview Avenue, Akron, OH

5. 567 Coconut Drive, Miami, FL

Exercise 3

▶ **Goal:** *The student will learn to remember written information by breaking large groups of material into smaller, related units or categories.*

Read each item and chunk the information into two or more groups. Then repeat each group, first with a visual cue and then without. Repeat the groups until you have memorized the item.

Numbers

1. 3559090

2. 5510808

3. 8884545

4. 2249868

5. 3326060

Addresses

1. 61 N. Bradley Road, Mission Hills, KS

2. 220 First Street, Oklahoma City, OK

3. 56 N. Mission Avenue, Milwaukee, WI

4. 10 E. Sally Lane, Austin, TX

5. 1 Dublin Court, Denver, CO

Exercise 4

▶ **Goal:** *The student will learn to remember written information by breaking large groups of material into smaller, related units or categories.*

Read each item and chunk the information into two or more groups. Then repeat each group, first with a visual cue and then without. Repeat the groups until you have memorized the item.

Numbers

1. 3515151

2. 4567070

3. 7683232

4. 2569090

5. 4952929

Addresses

1. 59 Lullaby Road, Palo Alto, CA

2. 34 East 51st Street, New York, NY

3. 98 First Street, San Diego, CA

4. 21 Cynthia Court, Dayton, OH

5. 6 Domino Boulevard, Boise, ID

Exercise 5

▶ **Goal:** *The student will learn to remember written information by breaking large groups of material into smaller, related units or categories.*

Read each item and chunk the information into two or more groups. Then repeat each group, first with a visual cue and then without. Repeat the groups until you have memorized the item.

Numbers

1. 4567890

2. 3145640

3. 6533850

4. 7895640

5. 2548960

Addresses

1. 99 Temple Road, Portland, OR 97035

2. 23 Aqua Blue Court, Los Angeles, CA 90278

3. 51 Center Street, Marblehead, MA 01945

4. 78 N. 21st Avenue, Bend, OR 97701

5. 28 E. Southern Road, Rochester Hills, MI 48309

Exercise 6

▶ **Goal:** *The student will learn to remember written information by breaking large groups of material into smaller, related units or categories.*

Read each item and chunk the information into two or more groups. Then repeat each group, first with a visual cue and then without. Repeat the groups until you have memorized the item.

Numbers

1. 8543899

2. 9328755

3. 2914588

4. 3784500

5. 6439877

Addresses

1. 415 Newcastle Dr., Minneapolis, MN 55412

2. 900 Pennsylvania St., Oklahoma City, OK 73519

3. 922 Southeast Central Ave., Hollywood, FL 33020

4. 544 Lake Dr., Chicago, IL 60611

5. 231 Cabrillo Ave., San Francisco, CA 94122

Exercise 7

▶ **Goal:** *The student will learn to remember written information by breaking large groups of material into smaller, related units or categories.*

Read each item and chunk the information into two or more groups. Then repeat each group, first with a visual cue and then without. Repeat the groups until you have memorized the item.

Numbers

1. 7653241

2. 3498653

3. 2908567

4. 3419538

5. 3873920

Addresses

1. 1450 Soundview Dr., University Place, WA 98466

2. 8972 Via de la Valle, Tallahassee, FL 32317

3. 64512 River Way, Hartford, CT 06112

4. 1677 Raft Place, Reno, NV 89509

5. 61139 River Ct., Charlottesville, VA 22904

Exercise 8

▶ **Goal:** *The student will learn to remember written information by breaking large groups of material into smaller, related units or categories.*

Read each item and chunk the information into two or more groups. Then repeat each group, first with a visual cue and then without. Repeat the groups until you have memorized the item.

Numbers

1. 8012743567

2. 8234116726

3. 7326746390

4. 2568760965

5. 6249000871

Addresses

1. 8934 First St., Scottsdale, AZ 85282

2. 5678 Shelly Hwy., Issaquah, WA 98027

3. 9843 Newberry Rd., Portolla Valley, CA 94028

4. 212 60th Ave., Milwaukee, WI 53022

5. 1981 Blue Dr., Seattle, WA 98198

Exercise 9

▶ **Goal:** *The student will learn to remember written information by breaking large groups of material into smaller, related units or categories.*

Read each item and chunk the information into two or more groups. Then repeat each group, first with a visual cue and then without. Repeat the groups until you have memorized the item.

Numbers

1. 4594039999

2. 2935746576

3. 2239348111

4. 9807754126

5. 5655574912

Addresses

1. 2908 Maplewood Dr., Kent, OH 44240

2. 1215 Selby Ln., Atherton, CA 94027

3. 347 Davis Blvd., Denver, CO 80210

4. 2209 Acorn St., Ann Arbor, MI 48104

5. 4371 4th St., Atlanta, GA 30308

Exercise *10*

▶ **Goal:** *The student will learn to remember written information by breaking large groups of material into smaller, related units or categories.*

Read each item and chunk the information into two or more groups. Then repeat each group, first with a visual cue and then without. Repeat the groups until you have memorized the item.

Numbers

1. 8007410122

2. 2124454432

3. 8726311040

4. 4258339087

5. 6083548889

Addresses

1. 234 Fifth Ave., New York, NY 10101

2. 4903 Shirley Ct., Baltimore, MD 21290

3. 1112 East Post St., Harlan, IA 51593

4. 5433 Clayton Rd., Wilmington, DE 19850

5. 2310 Lance Way SW, Ft. Worth, TX 76102

Acronyms & Silly Sentences

▶ **Goal:** *The student will learn to remember written lists of related words.*

Have the student create acronyms (words formed from the initial letters of a name or from several related words) or silly sentences. Use the following examples to show the student how acronyms and silly sentences aid memory. Then have the student complete the exercises on pages 118-127.

Acronyms

School Subjects

Math
English
Social **S**tudies

Acronym or Silly Sentence: _MESS_

Government Agency

National **A**eronautics and **S**pace **A**dministration

Acronym or Silly Sentence: _NASA_

Silly Sentence

How Living Things are Classified

Kingdom
Phylum
Class
Order
Family
Genus
Species

Acronym or Silly Sentence: _King Plays Checkers On Funny Girl's Stomach_

Exercise 1

▶ **Goal:** *The student will learn to remember written lists of related words.*

Use the words to create an acronym or silly sentence.

Class Activity

Drop
Everything
And
Read

Acronym or Silly Sentence: _____

_____

_____

Life Skills

Caring
Attitude
Responsibility
Effort

Acronym or Silly Sentence: _____

_____

_____

Exercise 2

▶ **Goal:** *The student will learn to remember written lists of related words.*

Use the words to create an acronym or silly sentence.

Seven Dwarfs

Sleepy
Doc
Bashful
Happy
Sneezy
Dopey
Grumpy

Acronym or Silly Sentence: _____

_____

_____

Oceans

Arctic
Atlantic
Indian
Pacific
Southern

Acronym or Silly Sentence: _____

_____

_____

Exercise 3

▶ **Goal:** *The student will learn to remember written lists of related words.*

Use the words to create an acronym or silly sentence.

Proofreading

Capitalization
Overall appearance
Punctuation
Spelling

Acronym or Silly Sentence: _____

_____

_____

Process of Division

Divide
Multiply
Subtract
Bring down

Acronym or Silly Sentence: _____

_____

_____

Exercise *4*

▶ **Goal:** *The student will learn to remember written lists of related words.*

Use the words to create an acronym or silly sentence.

Recreational Activity

Self-Contained Underwater Breathing Apparatus

Acronym or Silly Sentence: _____

_____

_____

Story Elements

Introduction
Detail
Detail
Detail
Conclusion
Transition words

Acronym or Silly Sentence: _____

_____

_____

Exercise 5

▶ **Goal:** *The student will learn to remember written lists of related words.*

Use the words to create an acronym or silly sentence.

Clouds

Cumulus, Nimbus, Stratus, Cirrus

Acronym or Silly Sentence: _____

_____

_____

Planets

Mercury
Venus
Earth
Mars
Jupiter
Saturn
Uranus
Neptune

Acronym or Silly Sentence: _____

_____

_____

Exercise 6

> **Goal:** *The student will learn to remember written lists of related words.*

Use the words to create an acronym or silly sentence.

Colors of the Rainbow

Red, Orange, Yellow, Green, Blue, Indigo, Violet

Acronym or Silly Sentence: _____

_____

_____

Trees

Fir, Redwood, Oak, Maple, Pine, Apple, Willow

Acronym or Silly Sentence: _____

_____

_____

Exercise *7*

▶ **Goal:** *The student will learn to remember written lists of related words.*

Use the words to create an acronym or silly sentence.

Great Lakes

Lake Superior
Lake Michigan
Lake Erie
Lake Ontario
Lake Huron

Acronym or Silly Sentence: _____

_____

_____

Native American Dwellings

Teepee, Adobe hut, Wigwam, Wooden lodge, Longhouse

Acronym or Silly Sentence: _____

_____

_____

Exercise 8

▶ **Goal:** *The student will learn to remember written lists of related words.*

Use the words to create an acronym or silly sentence.

Continents

North America, South America, Asia, Europe, Africa, Australia, Antarctica

Acronym or Silly Sentence: _____

_____

_____

First Six U.S. Presidents

Washington, Adams, Jefferson, Madison, Monroe, Adams

Acronym or Silly Sentence: _____

_____

_____

Exercise 9

▶ **Goal:** *The student will learn to remember written lists of related words.*

Use the words to create an acronym or silly sentence.

Simple Machines

Inclined plane, Wedge, Level, Axle and wheel, Pulley

Acronym or Silly Sentence: _____

_____

_____

Countries in South America

Argentina   Guyana
Bolivia   Paraguay
Brazil   Peru
Chile   Suriname
Columbia   Uruguay
Ecuador   Venezuela
French Guiana

Acronym or Silly Sentence: _____

_____

_____

Exercise

▶ **Goal:** *The student will learn to remember written lists of related words.*

Use the words to create an acronym or silly sentence.

13 Original Colonies

Virginia
Massachusetts
New Hampshire
Maryland
Connecticut
Rhode Island
Delaware

North Carolina
South Carolina
New Jersey
New York
Pennsylvania
Georgia

Acronym or Silly Sentence: _____

_____

_____

Confederate States During the Civil War

Alabama
Arkansas
Florida
Georgia
Louisiana
Mississippi

North Carolina
South Carolina
Tennessee
Texas
Virginia

Acronym or Silly Sentence: _____

_____

_____

Defining & Drawing

▶ **Goal:** *The student will learn to remember and recall vocabulary words using context clues and/or visual cues.*

Have the student define each word and draw a picture or write a sentence (real or silly) to remember the vocabulary words. The words in the exercises on pages 129-138 have been taken from the curriculum and daily life activities. Encourage students to use a dictionary or the Internet, or to ask someone to help them if they are unfamiliar with a word. The first one on each page has been done as an example.

Exercise 1

▶ **Goal:** *The student will learn to remember and recall vocabulary words using context clues and/or visual cues.*

Read each word aloud and write the definition in the space provided. If you need help with the definition, use a dictionary, look it up on the computer, or ask someone. Then create a sentence or drawing to help you remember it. The first one is done for you.

Word	Definition	Sentence/Drawing
nose	body part used for smelling	
snake		
ruler		
sad		
nail		

Exercise *2*

▶ **Goal:** *The student will learn to remember and recall vocabulary words using context clues and/or visual cues.*

Read each word aloud and write the definition in the space provided. If you need help with the definition, use a dictionary, look it up on the computer, or ask someone. Then create a sentence or drawing to help you remember it. The first one is done for you.

Word	Definition	Sentence/Drawing
fog	thick mist in the air close to the ground	The frog got lost in the FOG because he couldn't see.
meal		
base		
large		
deck		

Exercise 3

▶ **Goal:** *The student will learn to remember and recall vocabulary words using context clues and/or visual cues.*

Read each word aloud and write the definition in the space provided. If you need help with the definition, use a dictionary, look it up on the computer, or ask someone. Then create a sentence or drawing to help you remember it. The first one is done for you.

Word	Definition	Sentence/Drawing
grin	smile	When I win, it makes me GRIN.
anchor		
round		
shrink		
hurry		

Exercise 4

▶ **Goal:** *The student will learn to remember and recall vocabulary words using context clues and/or visual cues.*

Read each word aloud and write the definition in the space provided. If you need help with the definition, use a dictionary, look it up on the computer, or ask someone. Then create a sentence or drawing to help you remember it. The first one is done for you.

Word	Definition	Sentence/Drawing
creek	a very small river	The bird with a beak took a bath in the CREEK.
brave		
least		
gift		
haul		

Exercise 5

▶ **Goal:** *The student will learn to remember and recall vocabulary words using context clues and/or visual cues.*

Read each word aloud and write the definition in the space provided. If you need help with the definition, use a dictionary, look it up on the computer, or ask someone. Then create a sentence or drawing to help you remember it. The first one is done for you.

Word	Definition	Sentence/Drawing
gown	a fancy dress	The girl in the brown GOWN had a frown.
discover		
cellar		
narrow		
ache		

Visual Memory: Defining & Drawing
No-Glamour Memory

133

Copyright © 2007 LinguiSystems, Inc.

Exercise 6

▶ **Goal:** *The student will learn to remember and recall vocabulary words using context clues and/or visual cues.*

Read each word aloud and write the definition in the space provided. If you need help with the definition, use a dictionary, look it up on the computer, or ask someone. Then create a sentence or drawing to help you remember it. The first one is done for you.

Word	Definition	Sentence/Drawing
launch	throw or set off with great strength	Bill LAUNCHED the ball and it landed in the basket.
divide		
palace		
beverage		
boring		

Exercise 7

▶ **Goal:** *The student will learn to remember and recall vocabulary words using context clues and/or visual cues.*

Read each word aloud and write the definition in the space provided. If you need help with the definition, use a dictionary, look it up on the computer, or ask someone. Then create a sentence or drawing to help you remember it. The first one is done for you.

Word	Definition	Sentence/Drawing
fierce	very mean or violent	Even the FIERCE lion was scared by the storm.
vase		
rare		
reptile		
success		

Exercise 8

▶ **Goal:** *The student will learn to remember and recall vocabulary words using context clues and/or visual cues.*

Read each word aloud and write the definition in the space provided. If you need help with the definition, use a dictionary, look it up on the computer, or ask someone. Then create a sentence or drawing to help you remember it. The first one is done for you.

Word	Definition	Sentence/Drawing
hefty	powerful, strong	Lefty Lou hit a HEFTY home run out of the park.
lavender		
hedge		
polish		
prepare		

Exercise 9

▶ **Goal:** *The student will learn to remember and recall vocabulary words using context clues and/or visual cues.*

Read each word aloud and write the definition in the space provided. If you need help with the definition, use a dictionary, look it up on the computer, or ask someone. Then create a sentence or drawing to help you remember it. The first one is done for you.

Word	Definition	Sentence/Drawing
crumble	to break into small pieces	The cookie took a tumble and began to CRUMBLE.
special		
wealthy		
disagree		
frightened		

Exercise

▶ **Goal:** *The student will learn to remember and recall vocabulary words using context clues and/or visual cues.*

Read each word aloud and write the definition in the space provided. If you need help with the definition, use a dictionary, look it up on the computer, or ask someone. Then create a sentence or drawing to help you remember it. The first one is done for you.

Word	Definition	Sentence/Drawing
marine	having to do with the sea	Mary studies MARINE life in the Mediterranean Sea.
comedy		
aroma		
population		
handsome		

Graphing & Charting

▶ **Goal:** *The student will learn to remember written information by using visual aids and organizers.*

Provide paper and a pen or pencil to your student. Show the student the pages of graphing examples on pages 189-193. Use the example below to show the student how to graph using a pie chart.

Example: Mr. Burns owns a pet store. He has several kinds of animals for sale. He has more fish than anything else. Fish make up 35% of the animals in the store. Gerbils and hamsters make up 20%. Of the rest of the animals, 20% are birds, 10% are cats, 10% are dogs, and 5% are rabbits. (3.6 reading level)

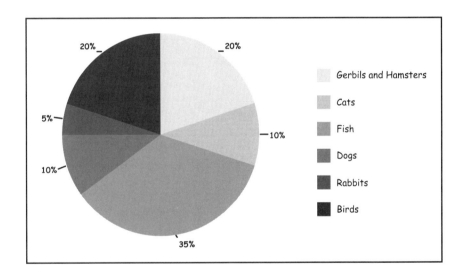

Give the student one of the exercises on pages 140-149. Have him read the information to identify the most appropriate chart, graph, or diagram to best display the information. Then have the student construct the graph, chart, or diagram using the information in the exercise. The student can use the graphing examples for help as needed.

Note: Reading levels are provided to help you choose appropriate passages for your students.

Exercise 1	0.0		Exercise 6	5.1
Exercise 2	0.7		Exercise 7	5.8
Exercise 3	2.3		Exercise 8	6.5
Exercise 4	3.7		Exercise 9	7.0
Exercise 5	4.7		Exercise 10	7.9

Exercise 1

▶ **Goal:** *The student will learn to remember written information by using visual aids and organizers.*

Read the information below. Determine which chart, graph, or diagram will best display the information. Then create the chart, graph, or diagram using the information.

Lucy	Max
5' 2"	5' 8"
12 years old	12 years old
blond	fair-haired
blue eyes	green eyes
swims	plays football
favorite subject: science	favorite subject: math
likes tacos	likes tacos and burritos

Exercise 2

▶ **Goal:** *The student will learn to remember written information by using visual aids and organizers.*

Read the information below. Determine which chart, graph, or diagram will best display the information. Then create the chart, graph, or diagram using the information.

Jenny has 2 dogs, 1 cat, and 3 fish.

Mark has 1 fish, 2 dogs, and no cats.

Nicky has 4 cats, 3 dogs, and 5 fish.

Benny has 3 cats, no fish, and 2 dogs.

Exercise 3

▶ **Goal:** *The student will learn to remember written information by using visual aids and organizers.*

Read the information below. Determine which chart, graph, or diagram will best display the information. Then create the chart, graph, or diagram using the information.

Main characters: Bree, a giant

Setting: England/land of giants/current times

Problem: Bree has been kidnapped by a giant.

Plot: Bree is taken to the giant's home. She is scared and wants to go home, but the giant will not let her leave.

Exercise 4

▶ **Goal:** *The student will learn to remember written information by using visual aids and organizers.*

Read the information below. Determine which chart, graph, or diagram will best display the information. Then create the chart, graph, or diagram using the information.

The sixth-grade class at Dayton Junior High needed to raise money for a class trip. They had one week to raise the $330 that would cover the cost of the field trip. They decided to sell candy bars. Each candy bar cost $2.

On Monday, they sold 45 candy bars. On Tuesday and Wednesday, they sold a total of 20 each day. Thursday, they sold 23 candy bars. Friday, they sold 65.

The students worked hard to meet their goal.

▶ **Goal:** *The student will learn to remember written information by using visual aids and organizers.*

Read the information below. Determine which chart, graph, or diagram will best display the information. Then create the chart, graph, or diagram using the information.

Mr. Freeze owns an ice-cream stand. Yesterday was a great day. Many people bought ice cream because it was very hot outside.

He sold 28 ice-cream bars, 15 Fudgsicles, 35 Sno-cones, and 40 Popsicles. He also sold 5 ice-cream sandwiches.

Next week, Mr. Freeze will be selling his ice cream from a truck. He needs to decide which kinds of ice cream to sell.

Exercise 6

▶ **Goal:** *The student will learn to remember written information by using visual aids and organizers.*

Read the information below. Determine which chart, graph, or diagram will best display the information. Then create the chart, graph, or diagram using the information.

Lynn wanted to find out what type of soda teenagers liked to drink. She created a survey and gave it to students in several of her classes. Forty-seven percent of the teenagers she asked liked Coke. Thirty-three percent chose Pepsi. Ten percent selected 7UP. Nine percent liked Dr. Pepper. Two percent didn't drink soda.

Exercise 7

▶ **Goal:** *The student will learn to remember written information by using visual aids and organizers.*

Read the information below. Determine which chart, graph, or diagram will best display the information. Then create the chart, graph, or diagram using the information.

Kate is in charge of planning the menu for the camping trip. She asked campers who went last year what their favorite foods were. They liked grilled cheese sandwiches, turkey sandwiches, chips, pancakes, tuna casserole, blueberry muffins, hot dogs, and s'mores. Their ideas will help Kate decide what to bring this year.

Exercise 8

▶ **Goal:** *The student will learn to remember written information by using visual aids and organizers.*

Read the information below. Determine which chart, graph, or diagram will best display the information. Then create the chart, graph, or diagram using the information.

Rural and urban communities are both desirable places to live although they are very different from one another. A rural area has a smaller population and open spaces. Houses are far apart. There are forests and farms instead of tall buildings. In contrast, an urban area is a town or city with a larger population. It is a built-up area that has many shops and services. An urban area has more homes, schools, and offices. It has more social and civic functions. A network of roads and other means of transportation run through this region.

Exercise 9

▶ **Goal:** *The student will learn to remember written information by using visual aids and organizers.*

Read the information below. Determine which chart, graph, or diagram will best display the information. Then create the chart, graph, or diagram using the information.

> One theme in Shakespeare's "Romeo and Juliet" is *Love as a Cause of Violence*. Tybalt realizes that Romeo has crashed his feast. He decides to kill Romeo just as Romeo notices Juliet and falls in love. The love between the two seems to push them closer to violence as they consider suicide. Romeo threatens to take his own life after he has been banished from Verona and his love, Juliet. Juliet also pulls a knife in order to take her own life.

Exercise 10

▶ **Goal:** *The student will learn to remember written information by using visual aids and organizers.*

Read the information below. Determine which chart, graph, or diagram will best display the information. Then create the chart, graph, or diagram using the information.

The United States purchased the Louisiana Territory from France in 1803. The land was from the Mississippi River to the Rocky Mountains. It was more than 77,000 square miles. The United States paid $15 million for the land.

President Thomas Jefferson sent two men to Paris to negotiate the purchase of land on the lower Mississippi. He was surprised and pleased when the French offered the entire territory. The new land meant that the United States would double in size. There would be more land to settle and free navigation of the Mississippi River would be secured.

Identifying Key Concepts

▶ **Goal:** *The student will learn to remember information by selecting only the critical parts of written material.*

Review the five key *wh-* words: *who, what, where, when*, and *why*. You might want to write them down for the student. You may also want to use the passages in the exercises to practice the *wh-* questions.

Have the student read the passages in the exercises on pages 151-160. To help him identify the key concepts, encourage him to highlight or underline the critical information you ask for.

Note: Reading levels are provided to help you choose appropriate passages for your students.

Exercise 1	1. 1.4	Exercise 6	1. 5.4
	2. 1.9		2. 5.5
Exercise 2	1. 2.5	Exercise 7	1. 5.8
	2. 2.7		2. 6.0
Exercise 3	1. 3.3	Exercise 8	1. 6.1
	2. 3.4		2. 6.2
Exercise 4	1. 3.7	Exercise 9	1. 6.5
	2. 4.0		2. 6.5
Exercise 5	1. 4.5	Exercise 10	1. 7.3
	2. 4.6		2. 7.9

Exercise *1*

▶ **Goal:** *The student will learn to remember information by selecting only the critical parts of written material.*

Read the following passages and identify *who*.

1. It was a sunny day. Tara walked to the ocean. She stopped at the candy store. Mr. Watt was working. Tara bought lemon drops. Then Tara went to the coffee shop. She saw her friends, Rashi and Shawn.

    Who is this story about?

    Who did Tara see first?

    Who did Tara see at the coffee shop?

2. Mrs. Cross' class was going on an overnight camping trip. The students were going to hike and explore. Brooke did not want to go. She did not want to be away from her parents.

    Who is the teacher in the story?

    Who is the student that did not want to go on the camping trip?

Exercise 2

▶ **Goal:** *The student will learn to remember information by selecting only the critical parts of written material.*

Read the following passages and identify **what**.

1. The gardener was late this morning. Her truck had gotten a flat tire on the way over. As soon as she got to the house, she said she was sorry and got right to work. She mowed the lawn and then pulled weeds out of the garden. Thanks to her speedy work, she got done on time.

   What made the gardener late?

   What did the gardener do first at the house?

2. Kittens are fun to watch. They have so much energy! Kittens like to play. They will chase string or ribbon, and some like to play with catnip. After jumping, chasing, and licking, they nap. Kittens need lots of sleep to grow and be healthy. Even when they are sleeping, kittens are fun to watch.

   What do kittens like to do?

   What do kittens like to chase?

   What do kittens do after they play?

Exercise 3

▶ **Goal:** *The student will learn to remember information by selecting only the critical parts of written material.*

Read the following passages and identify **when**.

1. I am trying to decide if I should go to the game tonight. I would really love to attend the game because I love soccer, but I watched a game on TV last night and didn't get my homework done. I have a lot of homework tonight. Plus, I have soccer practice after school until 5. The game starts at 7. My best friend will be there and he is a good student. Maybe we could do some of our homework at the game. Should I go?

   When does soccer practice begin?

   When does the soccer game start?

2. Tests can bring on anxiety and stress. Here are some things you can do to relax. The week of the test, try to follow your regular daily routine. Create a study plan. Review your notes and rewrite or reduce your notes so they fit onto a page or a card. You might want to meet with a study group. You also need to get plenty of sleep. The morning of the test you should eat a balanced breakfast. It should be a mix of carbohydrates, protein, and fat, such as toast, eggs, and juice. You want to feel relaxed when you sit down to take the test, so make sure you review your notes and get to class on time.

   When should you rewrite your notes?

   When should you eat a balanced meal?

   When should you begin studying for a test?

Exercise 4

▶ **Goal:** *The student will learn to remember information by selecting only the critical parts of written material.*

Read the following passages and identify *where*.

1. When Harry Potter was a boy, he became an orphan. He was forced to live with his aunt, uncle, and cousin in England. They were not very nice to Harry. When Harry was 12, he was taken from his aunt and uncle's home and sent to Hogwarts School. This was a school for wizards and witches. There, Harry made new friends and learned how to cast spells and make potions. He also learned how to play Quidditch. Quidditch is played above the ground on broomsticks. Hogwarts School was a very unusual place!

   Where do Harry's aunt and uncle live?

   Where was Harry sent when he was 12?

2. Misty and her aunt found a lot of interesting things as they walked along the beach at Ocean Bluff. They found a bunch of shells, including a clam shell. They also found a starfish, some sea glass, and a lobster claw. As they walked, they also found an old shoe, two plastic shovels, and one dead jellyfish. Misty looked into the shoe. Inside she found three hermit crabs crawling around. Misty wanted to take the crabs home. Her aunt said she had to leave the crabs at the beach where they belonged.

   Where were Misty and her aunt?

   Where did Misty find hermit crabs?

Exercise 5

> **Goal:** *The student will learn to remember information by selecting only the critical parts of written material.*

Read the following passages and identify **why**.

1. Hannah and Allie are good friends. They both like sports but Allie is a swimmer and Hannah plays tennis. They both like to hang out with their friends, but Hannah prefers to be with one or two friends at a time instead of with a large group. They both like to do art projects. Allie is a painter and Hannah is into making jewelry. Despite their differences, the girls get along well.

   Why do Hannah and Allie get along well?

   Why would Allie love to get a pool in her yard?

2. Rosh Hashanah is the Jewish New Year. It occurs in the fall, usually in September. This is one of the most important times for people who are Jewish. It marks the beginning of a ten-day period known as the High Holy Days. During Rosh Hashanah, a ram's horn is blown to welcome the new year. The ram's horn is known as a *shofar*. Apples and honey are eaten as a symbol of a wish for a sweet new year.

   Why is a ram's horn blown during Rosh Hashanah?

   Why are apples and honey eaten at the Jewish New Year?

Exercise

▶ **Goal:** *The student will learn to remember information by selecting only the critical parts of written material.*

Read the following passage and identify **where** and **what**.

1. When boats travel under the Golden Gate Bridge, they pass from the Pacific Ocean into the San Francisco Bay. Many people visit this bridge each year. The bridge was built in 1937. It is 1.7 miles long. Some people drive over the bridge, while others bike or walk over. If the weather is good, the views from the span are spectacular. Tourists can see the city, Alcatraz Island, the Bay Bridge, and more.

   Where do boats travel when they pass under the Golden Gate Bridge?

   What can tourists see from the Golden Gate Bridge?

Read the following passage and identify **what** and **why**.

2. This is the first year my family is not getting together for Easter. Instead, my step-dad, mom, and I are volunteering at a shelter for people who are homeless. We will get there early in the morning to help prepare the hams. Then we will work on the potatoes, salad, bread, and apple pies. I am excited to give back to the community. Volunteer work makes me feel good and it helps others. It's a win-win situation.

   What is this family planning to do this Easter?

   Why?

Exercise 7

▶ **Goal:** *The student will learn to remember information by selecting only the critical parts of written material.*

Read the following passages and identify **who** and **what**.

1. In 1620, people from England called *Pilgrims* came to America. The Pilgrims wanted freedom of religion. They wanted to choose their own church. The Pilgrims came to America on a ship called the *Mayflower*. They lived in a place called *Plymouth*. The Native Americans helped the Pilgrims find food and build homes.

   Who helped the Pilgrims when they arrived in America?

   What did the Pilgrims want to be able to choose?

2. Mr. Alt is a fifth-grade teacher. One of his duties is to prepare his students for their transition from elementary school to middle school. Mr. Alt knows that organization and planning are important skills for students to learn. To help students with this, each student uses a planner. The planners help students keep track of homework assignments. The planners are also used to communicate with parents. Students take their planners home each night for parents to sign. This way, Mr. Alt knows that parents are involved in their children's school work.

   Who is a fifth-grade teacher?

   What are two important skills for students to learn?

Exercise 8

▶ **Goal:** *The student will learn to remember information by selecting only the critical parts of written material.*

Read the following passage and identify **where** and **what**.

1. Newborn babies often sleep 16-17 hours a day. They may sleep in a bassinet, car seat, swing, stroller, or with their parents. As they get older, their sleep becomes more like adult sleep and they need a quiet place to sleep. At one year of age, children typically take one or two naps in the daytime and sleep in a crib. By three years of age, some children no longer require a nap and sleep about 10 hours at night.

   Where do newborn babies sleep?

   What do newborn babies do most of the time?

Read the following passage and identify **when** and **why**.

2. Families often get together during holidays. Many people have time off, so they travel to be with their families. One of the most popular holidays for families to be together is Thanksgiving. Some people fly to see their families. Some people drive. The busiest days to travel are the Wednesday before Thanksgiving and the Sunday after. There is a lot of traffic on the highways and the airports are crowded. It is nice when you can stay home and have your family visit you!

   When do many people travel to see their families?

   Why is there a lot of traffic on the highways during the Thanksgiving holiday?

Exercise 9

▶ **Goal:** *The student will learn to remember information by selecting only the critical parts of written material.*

Read the following passages and identify *where*, *what*, and *why*.

1. Elections for student council were held today at school. Serena was running for president. At the end of the day, the results were posted outside the school office. When Serena looked at the results, she began to cry. She turned around and saw Jason, a classmate who was also running for president, yelling and pumping his fist with delight.

   Where were elections for student council held?

   What was Serena running for?

   Why did Serena cry?

   Why was Jason yelling with delight?

2. Walt Disney World in Orlando, Florida and Family Adventures in Yellowstone National Park are two popular places for families to visit. Walt Disney World has four huge theme parks. It also has two water parks. There is much to do at Family Adventures. Families can camp, hike, raft, and ride horses. This park also has guides to give tours. The guides will talk about the history of the area and its wildlife. They can also give instruction on how to do an activity safely.

   Where is Walt Disney World?

   What does Walt Disney World have to offer?

   Why would a tourist in Yellowstone hire a guide?

Exercise

▶ **Goal:** *The student will learn to remember information by selecting only the critical parts of written material.*

Read the following passage and identify **who**, **what**, and **why**.

1. Driving requires attention and concentration. Regardless of weather, drivers should be focused on the road with both hands on the wheel. This means that talking on the phone and fiddling with the radio are out. Both of these activities detract from driving. For your safety and the safety of others, it is important to give the road 100% of your attention.

   Who is the intended audience of this paragraph?

   What should good drivers do?

   Why is it important to stay focused on the road when driving?

Read the following passage and identify **who**, **what**, **when**, **where**, and **why**.

2. Students who plan to go to college should being planning for it at the end of eighth grade. Before high school, students need to decide which classes they will need to complete by their senior year. Many colleges have requirements for math, English, and science. Guidance counselors can help with class selections and answer questions about colleges. Students must also take standardized tests, such as the SAT or ACT. These tests are given throughout the year at schools around the country. High test scores and good grades are important for getting into college. However, participation in student government, sports, performing arts, and community service can also help a student get into the college of his choice.

   Who can help answer questions about colleges?

   What are the main determiners for entrance into many colleges?

   When should students begin planning to attend college?

   Where are the standardized tests given?

   Why should students plan in advance if they want to attend college?

Visualizing

▶ **Goal:** *The student will learn to remember written information by using more than one modality.*

Have the student read the word, sentence, or paragraph. Instruct the student to create a mental picture of the word, sentence, or paragraph. Then have the student describe in detail what he is picturing.

To help students with this task, ask the student to draw a picture and explain the image. Eliminate the drawing as soon as the student is able to remember the word or the general concept of the sentence or paragraph. The words below can also be used as cues to help students remember what they have heard.

Cue Words		
who	color	texture
what	size	mood
where	shape	movement
when	number	sound

Note: Reading levels for the paragraphs are provided to help you choose appropriate passages for your students.

Exercise 1	1.4	Exercise 6	5.1
Exercise 2	2.7	Exercise 7	5.5
Exercise 3	3.5	Exercise 8	6.2
Exercise 4	4.0	Exercise 9	6.3
Exercise 5	4.4	Exercise 10	6.7

Exercise 1

Goal: *The student will learn to remember written information by using more than one modality.*

Read each word, sentence, or paragraph. Create a picture in your mind of what you hear. Then describe in detail what you are picturing.

Word

bug

Sentence

The bug flew right by his ear.

Paragraph

Danny ate lunch at noon. He had macaroni and cheese, carrot sticks, and milk. Danny took his food out on the porch. The sun was warm. When Danny sat down to eat, a bug flew right by his ear and then by his food. He tried to catch the bug, but it got away. As Danny ate his lunch, he looked for more bugs.

▶ **Goal:** *The student will learn to remember written information by using more than one modality.*

Read each word, sentence, or paragraph. Create a picture in your mind of what you hear. Then describe in detail what you are picturing.

Word

ran

Sentence

Carrie almost ran into the dog, Jack, from down the street.

Paragraph

This morning, Carrie went for a bike ride around the neighborhood. She saw lots of people. First she saw the little redheaded girl next door. Then Carrie almost ran into the dog, Jack, from down the street. Jack barked and ran next to her as she rode. When Carrie turned the corner, she waved at Neil. Neil was a pilot. He had on his uniform and was putting his suitcase into his car. A mile down the street, Carrie saw a worker wearing a hard hat. As Carrie rode home, Jack went into his yard. Carrie smiled at Jack's owner. When Carrie got home, she was tired.

Exercise 3

▶ **Goal:** *The student will learn to remember written information by using more than one modality.*

Read each word, sentence, or paragraph. Create a picture in your mind of what you hear. Then describe in detail what you are picturing.

Word

ring

Sentence

A ring is formed for each year of a tree's life.

Paragraph

Trees can grow and thrive for hundreds of years. The age of a tree can be determined by the number of rings counted in a cross-section of trunk. A ring is formed for each year of a tree's life. The circumference of the tree trunk and the tree's height increase with age. Older trees are valuable.

Exercise 4

▶ **Goal:** *The student will learn to remember written information by using more than one modality.*

Read each word, sentence, or paragraph. Create a picture in your mind of what you hear. Then describe in detail what you are picturing.

Word

attention

Sentence

Not paying attention to anything on the ground, Jen tripped over a large rock.

Paragraph

Jen had just gotten home after a hard day at work. To relax, she set out on a five-mile run through the park. As she ran, she noticed the leaves changing colors and the wonderful smells of autumn. It was her favorite time of year. Not paying attention to anything on the ground, Jen tripped over a large rock. She fell straight onto the sandy gravel. With scrapes on her hands and knees, Jen managed to limp home.

Exercise 5

▶ **Goal:** *The student will learn to remember written information by using more than one modality.*

Read each word, sentence, or paragraph. Create a picture in your mind of what you hear. Then describe in detail what you are picturing.

Word

pyramid

Sentence

The orange section of the food pyramid is for grains.

Paragraph

The food pyramid is a guide to promote healthy eating. It was revised in 2005 and is currently made up of six different colors. The orange section is for grains. A person should eat at least three ounces of whole grains each day. The green stands for vegetables. Dark green and orange vegetables, dry beans, and peas are good choices of vegetables. The red indicates fruits. Eat a variety of fresh, frozen, canned, or dried fruit every day. The yellow stands for oils. It is recommended that a person limits food with oils, such as nuts, because of the amount of fat in them. The blue represents milk. Eat calcium-rich foods but make sure they are low-fat or fat-free. Finally, the purple is for meat and beans. Choose lean or low-fat meat and bake it, broil it, or grill it.

Exercise 6

▶ **Goal:** *The student will learn to remember written information by using more than one modality.*

Read each word, sentence, or paragraph. Create a picture in your mind of what you hear. Then describe in detail what you are picturing.

Word

thief

Sentence

Alarms and dogs are the best way to keep a thief out of your home.

Paragraph

Sally Lent's home had recently been broken into. The thief had broken the window on the back door. He had taken the TV, DVD player, and stereo system. When Sally saw what had happened, she called the police. Then she called her friend Steve Jones, a detective, to help with home safety. Detective Jones suggested that Sally buy an alarm system and possibly a dog. "Alarms and dogs are the best way to keep a thief out of your home," stressed the detective.

Exercise 7

▶ **Goal:** *The student will learn to remember written information by using more than one modality.*

Read each word, sentence, or paragraph. Create a picture in your mind of what you hear. Then describe in detail what you are picturing.

Word

baby

Sentence

The adorable baby girl slept in her stroller.

Paragraph

On a warm Sunday morning, Maria took a walk with her baby around the neighborhood. The adorable baby girl slept in her stroller while her mom pushed her up and down the streets. Twenty minutes into their walk, the sky turned dark. Maria decided to head home. Maria walked quickly, watching the sky as she walked. Just as Maria and her baby entered the garage, the rain began. Maria and her baby were safe and dry.

Exercise 8

▶ **Goal:** *The student will learn to remember written information by using more than one modality.*

Read each word, sentence, or paragraph. Create a picture in your mind of what you hear. Then describe in detail what you are picturing.

Word

tornado

Sentence

Winds from a tornado can reach up to 300 miles per hour.

Paragraph

Tornadoes are one of nature's most violent storms. Tornadoes can be very dangerous—sometimes even deadly. A tornado is a rotating, funnel-shaped cloud. Winds from a tornado can reach up to 300 miles per hour. It usually begins during a thunderstorm. A tornado causes damage when it touches down on the ground. It can damage an area up to one mile wide and 50 miles long. The most common time for tornadoes to form is spring and summer. It is hard to predict a tornado. Usually a city will have a few minutes of warning. The most important thing to do when a tornado is nearby is to take shelter.

Visual Memory: Visualizing
No-Glamour Memory 169

Exercise *9*

▶ **Goal:** *The student will learn to remember written information by using more than one modality.*

Read each word, sentence, or paragraph. Create a picture in your mind of what you hear. Then describe in detail what you are picturing.

Word

jack-o'-lantern

Sentence

A jack-o'-lantern is made when a face is carved into a hollow pumpkin.

Paragraph

Before there were flashlights, people in Ireland used to carve out turnips and put candles in them to make lanterns. When the people came to America, they saw that there weren't many turnips. There were pumpkins, so those were used instead. This began the tradition of the jack-o'-lantern. A jack-o'-lantern is made when a face is carved into a hollow pumpkin. A lighted candle is placed inside to create the lantern. It is usually displayed on Halloween.

Exercise 10

▶ **Goal:** *The student will learn to remember written information by using more than one modality.*

Read each word, sentence, or paragraph. Create a picture in your mind of what you hear. Then describe in detail what you are picturing.

Word

villages

Sentence

The inhabitants of these villages spoke unique dialects and had their own customs.

Paragraph

In ancient Greece, villages were far away from each other. The people of the villages spoke their own versions of the same language. This means that people in one village couldn't understand people from another village. They also had their own customs. Communication between villages was limited due to distance, mountains, and rivers. Each village was like its own country.

Paraphrasing

▶ **Goal:** *The student will learn to remember information presented in written form by processing, comprehending, and paraphrasing material in her own words.*

Use the following examples to show the student how to paraphrase, or restate, words, a set of directions, or a paragraph.

Give the student a pen, a highlighter, and one of the exercises on pages 173-182. If the student is working at the word level, have her write a synonym for each word. If the student is working at the following directions or paragraph level, have her paraphrase the directions or paragraph. You may need a separate sheet of paper. Encourage the student to highlight or underline key words and ideas before paraphrasing the information.

Words

1. seat   <u>chair</u>

2. see   <u>look, view, stare, gaze</u>

Following Directions

1. Press the ON button. Wait for the screen to light up and look for the icons to pop up. Then click on the program you want to use.   (1.1 reading level)

   <u>Press the ON button. After the screen lights up and the icons pop up, click on the program you want to use.</u>

Paragraph

A fisherman's knot is used to join two thin fishing lines. The knot is made of two overhand knots, one holding the right-hand line and the other holding the left-hand line. Each overhand knot is pulled tightly. Then the whole knot is pulled tightly so the overhand knots come together.   (5.3 reading level)

<u>A fisherman's knot joins two fishing lines together by tying them with two overhand knots.</u>

Note: Reading levels are provided for the directions and paragraphs to help you choose appropriate passages for your students.

Exercise 1	1. 1.2	Exercise 4	1. 3.5	Exercise 7	1. 4.4	Exercise 9	1. 5.5
	2. 1.8		2. 3.6		2. 4.5		2. 5.4
Paragraph 1.9		Paragraph 3.6		Paragraph 4.8		Paragraph 5.8	
Exercise 2	1. 1.9	Exercise 5	1. 3.8	Exercise 8	1. 4.7	Exercise 10	1. 5.5
	2. 2.4		2. 3.8		2. 4.8		2. 5.6
Paragraph 3.0		Paragraph 4.0		Paragraph 4.9		Paragraph 6.4	
Exercise 3	1. 2.9	Exercise 6	1. 4.1				
	2. 3.3		2. 4.4				
Paragraph 3.2		Paragraph 4.7					

Exercise 1

> **Goal:** *The student will learn to remember information presented in written form by processing, comprehending, and paraphrasing material in her own words.*

Read each item. Give a synonym for each word. Paraphrase the directions and paragraph. It might help to highlight or underline key words and ideas.

Words

1. help _____

2. hurt _____

Following Directions

1. Remove the chess board and the pieces from the box. Find an opponent. Line up the pieces in two rows. The pawns are in front of the rooks, bishops, knights, queen, and king. Each piece can move in a different way. You win by taking the king.

   _____

   _____

2. To wash a car, you need water, a bucket, soap, and two clean cloths. Put a few drops of soap into the bucket and fill it with water. Then spray the car with water. Spread the soap on the car. Rinse the car well. Dry the windows and mirrors with a clean cloth so they don't spot.

   _____

   _____

Paragraph

Everyone met on the playground. We all brought yearbooks and items to sign. Some people had cameras. The PTA set up a table with sandwiches, chips, and apples for lunch. There was also a huge cake that looked like the school. It was cool! After the food, we played games and hung out. We all had fun on the last day of school.

_____

_____

Exercise 2

▶ **Goal:** *The student will learn to remember information presented in written form by processing, comprehending, and paraphrasing material in her own words.*

Read each item. Give a synonym for each word. Paraphrase the directions and paragraph. It might help to highlight or underline key words and ideas.

Words

1. evil _____

2. disappear _____

Following Directions

1. I'm hungry. Let me know if you see the concession guy coming around. I want a hot dog, peanuts, and a soda. If you don't see him in five minutes, please run up to the stand to get the food. I'll give you the money now. This game is so exciting; I just don't want to miss a minute of it!

   _____

   _____

2. Look at the page carefully. The notes fall either on the lines or in the spaces between the lines. They range from A to G. From top to bottom, the notes in the spaces are E, G, B, D, F. This can most easily be remembered using the phrase Every Good Boy Does Fine (EGBDF).

   _____

   _____

Paragraph

It was almost time for school to start. Trey needed to get his school supplies. His mom took him to the store. He had a list of things he needed for school. The list included a notebook, pencils, and paper. For art, he needed markers and scissors. Trey also needed to bring two rolls of paper towels.

   _____

   _____

Exercise 3

▶ **Goal:** *The student will learn to remember information presented in written form by processing, comprehending, and paraphrasing material in her own words.*

Read each item. Give a synonym for each word. Paraphrase the directions and paragraph. It might help to highlight or underline key words and ideas.

Words

1. respect _____

2. tight _____

Following Directions

1. To get to the museum, take a left on Rymer Drive. When you get to the second four-way stop sign, turn right onto Lilac Lane. Take Lilac Lane for a half mile until you see a gas station on the left. Turn right past the gas station and take a left onto State Street. Go straight until it dead ends. The museum is at the end.

   _____

   _____

2. Before your race, remember to loosen your muscles. You can stretch, jump up and down, and swing your arms around. After that, put your cap and goggles on. Step onto the racing block. Wait for the official to say, "Swimmers, take your mark . . .".

   _____

   _____

Paragraph

Brooke and her twin sister, Britt, had to decide what they wanted for their birthday dinner. Each year, the twins choose a meal and help their mother prepare it. This year, Brooke wanted spaghetti. Britt wanted chicken pot pie. To make the girls happy, their mother made both meals. She only made one birthday cake though!

_____

_____

Exercise 4

▶ **Goal:** *The student will learn to remember information presented in written form by processing, comprehending, and paraphrasing material in her own words.*

Read each item. Give a synonym for each word. Paraphrase the directions and paragraph. It might help to highlight or underline key words and ideas.

Words

1. babble _____

2. elated _____

Following Directions

1. Look at the first word in the list. Look at the first two or three letters in the word. Think about where those letters fall in the alphabet. Open the dictionary to the pages where the target letters are located. Search the page for the word. Once you locate the word, write the part of speech and the definition. Then use the word in a sentence.

_____

_____

2. Sort the lights and the darks into separate piles. Place the darks in the machine first. Set the dial to cold water. Set the water level to low because the load is small. Add a cup of detergent and close the lid. When the load is finished, be sure to remove all the athletic wear and the sweater so they can air dry.

_____

_____

Paragraph

Riding a bike with toe clips can be quite difficult, even for a biker with experience. First place one foot in the toe clip while the bike is leaning against a wall. Pull the strap on the toe clip until the clip is snug to your foot. However, make sure you can slide your foot in and out of the toe clip. Then sit on your bike. Start pedaling as you push away from the wall. Pedal a few times to get started. Flip the free pedal with your other foot to get the toe clip on top of the pedal. Place your toe in this clip so both feet are now in the toe clips. Ride your bike by pushing down on the pedals and pulling up on the toe clips.

_____

_____

Exercise 5

▶ **Goal:** *The student will learn to remember information presented in written form by processing, comprehending, and paraphrasing material in her own words.*

Read each item. Give a synonym for each word. Paraphrase the directions and paragraph. It might help to highlight or underline key words and ideas.

Words

1. intense _____

2. horrified _____

Following Directions

1. When you are training a dog, you will need a whistle, a leash, and a handful of treats. Find an open space outside or inside with no distractions. Some of the first instructions to teach include *sit*, *stay*, and *come*. Be patient and positive. Training a dog takes time.

_____

_____

2. I will be home by 10 o'clock. Please be careful while I am not home. I left several phone numbers taped to the fridge. If one of your sisters feels sick, go next door and ask Dr. Sarah to come over. She knows I am leaving for a while. If there is another kind of problem, you can call me on my cell phone. However, if there is an emergency, call 911 first.

_____

_____

Paragraph

The Detroit Tigers and Oakland A's are playing in the fourth game of the American League Championship Series. The score is tied in the bottom of the 9th. The fans are cheering loudly. One of the Tigers hits a three-run home run to win the game. The fans and players go wild! The Tigers sweep the A's four games to none and advance to the World Series for the first time in more than 20 years.

_____

_____

Exercise 6

▶ **Goal:** *The student will learn to remember information presented in written form by processing, comprehending, and paraphrasing material in her own words.*

Read each item. Give a synonym for each word. Paraphrase the directions and paragraph. It might help to highlight or underline key words and ideas.

Words

1. ask _____

2. refuse _____

Following Directions

1. At the grocery store, please buy milk, eggs, and flour. When you get home, follow the recipe marked in the cookbook for making a cake. The rest of the ingredients are in the pantry.

   _____

   _____

2. For dinner, we are going to make turkey chili. First we need to brown the ground turkey in a pan with some onion. Next we will add chili seasoning and tomato sauce. Then we will add chopped green and red peppers. We will mix it all together, bring it to a boil, and let it simmer for 20 minutes.

   _____

   _____

Paragraph

Frogs are amphibians. This means that they begin their lives in the water as tadpoles. In the water, they develop legs, lungs, and other body parts needed to survive on land. When they are ready, the tadpoles leave the water for land. The tails they used for swimming disappear and the frogs adapt to life on land.

_____

_____

Exercise 7

▶ **Goal:** *The student will learn to remember information presented in written form by processing, comprehending, and paraphrasing material in her own words.*

Read each item. Give a synonym for each word. Paraphrase the directions and paragraph. It might help to highlight or underline key words and ideas.

Words

1. conceited _____   2. sly _____

Following Directions

1. Students in fifth grade had to collect 20 different kinds of leaves for their science project. The leaves could come from their yards and local parks and playgrounds. Students had to mount their leaves onto a sheet of poster board. They also had to write a short description of each leaf. The posters were displayed in the hallway by their classrooms.

   _____

   _____

2. Divide the paper into four even squares. Draw a picture in each square that helps to tell a story. Use bubbles to show what the characters are thinking or saying. Color in the pictures when you are finished.

   _____

   _____

Paragraph

Each year, every state has a state fair. There are rides, shopping, and great entertainment at the state fair. Fair-goers can also try out many different kinds of foods. Favorite foods are corn dogs and caramel corn. There is something for everyone!

   _____

   _____

Exercise 8

▶ **Goal:** *The student will learn to remember information presented in written form by processing, comprehending, and paraphrasing material in her own words.*

Read each item. Give a synonym for each word. Paraphrase the directions and paragraph. It might help to highlight or underline key words and ideas.

Words

1. general _____

2. trust _____

Following Directions

1. Unlock the doors and let the people in. Turn on the microphone and ask if anyone is new. Request that new members move to the front of the room in order to have a better view. Begin the warm-up with energetic music.

_____

_____

2. After dinner, rinse the dishes and load them into the dishwasher. Then wipe off the counters and sweep the floor. After you take out the trash, start your homework.

_____

_____

Paragraph

Some people claim that breakfast is the most important meal of the day. The body needs energy in the morning to get it going. Many people eat sweet foods, such as cereal or muffins, because they have sugar in them. The sugar offers instant energy. This helps people wake up. If people wait to eat until lunch, their bodies are deprived of fuel and they may overeat. Small, regular meals are the healthiest way to eat.

_____

_____

Exercise 9

▶ **Goal:** *The student will learn to remember information presented in written form by processing, comprehending, and paraphrasing material in her own words.*

Read each item. Give a synonym for each word. Paraphrase the directions and paragraph. It might help to highlight or underline key words and ideas.

Words

1. dislodged _____

2. instant _____

Following Directions

1. It is easy to make banana pudding. You need one box of instant vanilla pudding mix. You also need milk, one can of condensed milk, a carton of whipped cream, and at least four bananas. For a special touch, you will also need a box of vanilla wafer cookies.

   _____

   _____

2. To make the banana pudding, follow the directions on the box of pudding mix. Set the mixture aside. Place one layer of vanilla wafers on the bottom of a large baking pan. Then slice the bananas. Put half of the sliced bananas and pudding mixture on top of the wafers. Then add another layer of vanilla wafers. Cover them with the rest of the bananas and pudding mixture. Chill until ready to serve.

   _____

   _____

Paragraph

The first flag for the United States was sewn by Betsy Ross. That flag was different from the one in use today. Like the current flag, the first flag had stars that stood for the states and stripes that stood for the 13 original colonies. However, back when Betsy Ross sewed the first flag, there were fewer states, so she sewed the stars in a circle.

_____

_____

Exercise 10

▶ **Goal:** *The student will learn to remember information presented in written form by processing, comprehending, and paraphrasing material in her own words.*

Read each item. Give a synonym for each word. Paraphrase the directions and paragraph. It might help to highlight or underline key words and ideas.

Words

1. extreme _____   2. overwhelmed _____

Following Directions

1. This week, your homework is to read pages 30-45 in your history book. Then write a short report on the causes of the Civil War. Your report is due on Friday.

   _____

   _____

2. Take the dessert out of the freezer 12 hours prior to serving. Let it thaw in the refrigerator. Before dinner, take the dessert out of the refrigerator. Set it on a counter or table to further thaw. Slice into pieces and top with whipped cream before eating.

   _____

   _____

Paragraph

The sun is by far the largest object in the solar system. It contains more than 99.8% of the total mass of the solar system. Right now, the sun is about 70% hydrogen, 28% helium, and 2% metals. These amounts are slowly changing.

_____

_____

Saying, Tracing, Writing, & Drawing Sounds

▶ **Goal:** *The student will learn to remember sounds and their corresponding written symbols.*

Help the student make flashcards for the uppercase and lowercase letters. A template is provided on page 184.

After the flashcards are made, have the student:

- **Say** the sound.

- **Trace** the sound with his finger or a pen or pencil.

- **Write** a word that contains the sound on the back of the flashcard. See pages 185-188 for suggested words.

- **Draw** a picture that corresponds with the sound on a separate sheet of paper. Then write the word in a sentence.

Groups I-VII in the uppercase and lowercase sections address letter reversals and sound/symbol confusion. Groups VIII-XIV in the lowercase letter section are more advanced and should be introduced when you believe it is developmentally appropriate for the student. It is recommended that the student learn the sounds in the order of the groups presented.

Uppercase Letters

Group I: C, F, G, H, J, K, L, R, T
Group II: B, D, P, Q
Group III: M, N
Group IV: S, Z
Group V: V, W, X, Y
Group VI: A, E, I, O, U

Lowercase Letters

Group I: c, f, g, h, j, k, l, r, t
Group II: b, d, p, q
Group III: m, n
Group IV: s, z
Group V: v, w, x, y
Group VI: ch, sh, th
Group VII: a, e, i, o, u

Group VIII: a_e, e_e, i_e, o_e, u_e (silent e)
Group IX: ai, ay, au, aw
Group X: ea, ee, ei, ey, ew, eu
Group XI: ie
Group XII: oa, oe, oi, oy, $\overline{oo}$ (*book*), oo (*loop*), ou, ow
Group XIII: ia, ue, ui
Group XIV: ar, or, er, ir, ur

Flashcard Template

Suggested Words for Letters

Note: The sounds in the word lists may have different pronunciations (e.g., *oa = boat, broad*)

a

act
active
address
after
ant
apple
ask
at
cat
hat
map
sand
tan
tap

b

baby
back
bad
ball
balloon
banana
bat
bed
bee
belly
belt
bench
big
book

c

cake
call
cap
cat
clean

clear
cleat
clock
coat
consonant
cook
cot
cover
cup

d

dab
date
desk
diaper
diary
dig
digit
disk
dog
draw
dream
drift
dust

e

Ed
effort
elbow
elephant
elf
enchilada
envelope
every
pet
seven
Ted
ten

f

fan
fast
fat
fire
fish
fix
flat
flea
foam
fog
foot
free
Friday
friend
fun

g

garden
gas
gate
get
gift
girl
glass
glide
go
goal
goat
gold
goose
grass

h

hat
heat
heavy

hike
hill
hip
home
homework
hook
horse
hot
human
hut

i

igloo
ignore
in
issue
it
itch
flip
hit
listen
rim
ship
sip
skin
tin
tip
trip

j

jam
jaw
jazz
jeep
jelly
jet
jingle

job
joint
joke
jolly
journal
juggle
jump

k

kangaroo
keep
key
kickstand
kid
kind
king
kiss
kitchen
kite
kitten
koala

l

lake
lamp
land
law
left
lemon
let
library
like
limp
line
lip
live
log

m

major
make
map
March
meet
met
miss
mistake
mitt
mole
mom
Monday

n

nap
near
neat
nest
never
next
nice
night
nine
noodle
noon
nose
note
nut

o

occupy
ocelot
octagon
October
odd
off
olive
on

operate
Oscar
ostrich

p

pan
parent
park
pass
pat
peak
pen
penny
people
pick
pickle
pile
pit
pot

q

quack
quarter
queen
question
quick
quiet
quilt
quit
quiver
quote

r

rag
rash
raw
read
red
repair

rest
ribbon
rice
right
rip
rock
rug
run
rust

s

sad
Sally
sat
saw
single
sip
slice
snap
snuggle
sock
soft
sore
soup
sour
sun

t

take
talk
tall
tan
teacher
ten
test
tight
tip
tongue
tonight

tooth
top
turn
tusk

u

ugly
umbrella
umpire
under
unlock
until
unzip
up
brush
fun
Sunday

v

vacation
vacuum
valentine
van
vat
vegetable
vehicle
veil
vein
very
vet

w

wag
walk
wander
wash
water
welcome

well
west
wet
white
window
wish

x

excite
experience
extra
X-ray

y

yak
yam
yard
yawn
year
yes
yesterday
yet
yip
yoga
yolk
young
your

z

zany
zap
zebra
Zed
zero
zillion
zip
zone
zoo
zoom

Visual Memory: Saying, Tracing, Writing, & Drawing Sounds
No-Glamour Memory

Suggested Words for Sounds

ch

chain
chalk
change
chat
cheap
cherry
chess
chick
chip
chocolate
choke

sh

shake
she
shine
ship
shirt
shiver
shock
shoe
shore
shot
shoulder
show
shrub

th

that
the
they
thin
thing
think
third
this
thistle
thorn

three
throw
Thursday

a_e

Abe
ace
ape
ate
escape
fate
Kate
late
mate
Nate
plate
slate
trace

e_e

delete
deplete
extreme

i_e

abide
bite
bribe
ice
kite
like
mice
pipe
ripe
side
site
tile
tribe

o_e

code
hole
home
ignore
robe
rope
scope
tote
whole

u_e

cute
lure
mule
use

ai

aim
bait
brain
complain
contain
plain
rain
refrain
stain
train

ay

bay
clay
crayon
day
lay
may
pay

play
ray
say
stay
stray
tray

au/aw

auction
author
caught
laugh
awful
caw
crawfish
draw
drawn
gnaw
law
raw
saw

ea

beam
beat
cream
defeat
ear
eat
gleam
mean
meat
ream
seam
seat
team
treat

ee

beet
between
bleep
creep
fleet
meet
peep
seep
sheep
sheet

ei

ceiling
either

ey

hey
honey
monkey
whey

eu/ew

euphoria
Europe
blew
crew
dew
drew
few
flew
grew
sew

ie

achieve
believe
convenient

cried
friend
lie
movie
pie
tried

oa

approach
board
boat
broad
coat
float
soar
toad

oe

doe
foe
mistletoe
poet
toe

oi

asteroid
avoid
boil
coil
coin
Detroit
foil
joint
oil
point
soil
toil
turmoil

oy

toy
boy
soy
coy
convoy
joy
enjoy
Troy
ploy
alloy

o͞o

book
cook
crook
look
shook
soot
took

oo

broom
coop
fool
loony
loop
loose
loot
pool
school
shoot
stool
tool
yahoo
zoo

ou

about
account
count
four
ground
group
our
out
round
sound

ow

bow
brow
chow
clown
cow
flow
flower
frown
how
low
mow

ia

dial
diamond
trial
vial

ue

blue
cue
dues
ensue
glue
queue
sue
true
value

ui

guide
juice
suit

plow
powder
power
sow
stow
throw

ar

bar
car
far
farm
large
Mars
scarf
start
tar
tarp

or

acorn
actor
bored
corn
for
forge
gorge
port
report
scorn
stubborn
sword

er

deserve
fern
flower
gerbil
germ
jerk
perfect
serpent
stern
swerve
teacher

ir

birch
bird
birth
fir
firm
flirt
girl
skirt
squirm
squirrel
swirl
twirl

ur

absurd
burn
curl
fur
hurl
lurch
purchase
security
slurp
survive
turn

Graphing & Charting Examples

1. **Pie Chart:** used to show percentage relationships or parts of a whole; no more than eight segments recommended

   Example: how your income is spent

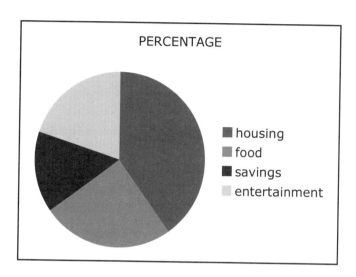

2. **Bar Graph:** used to show data or relationships and comparisons

   Example: the number of students per grade at Bethen Elementary School

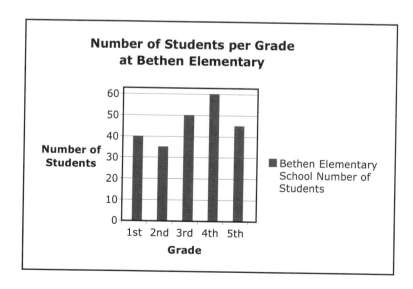

3. **Line Graph:** used to show trends or performance over time

   Example: the population of the world from 1800 A.D. to 2000 A.D.

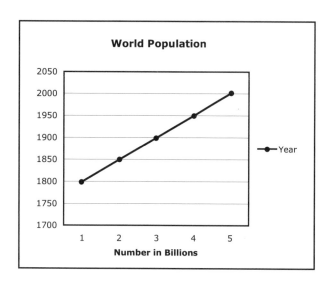

4. **Outline:** used to organize related information by main topic and details

   Example: what you eat in a day

Daily Food Consumption
I.   breakfast
     A. cereal
     B. milk
     C. orange juice
II. Snack
     A. apple
     B. peanut butter
III. Lunch
     A. sandwich
     B. chips
     C. orange
     D. gummy candy
     E. milk

IV. Snack
    A. carrot sticks
    B. pretzels
V. Dinner
    A. chicken
    B. potato
    C. broccoli
    D. salad
    E. candy bar

190

5. **Venn Diagram:** used to compare and contrast information

   Example: the similarities and differences between San Francisco and Los Angeles

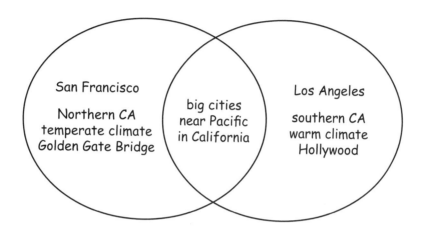

6. **Web Diagram:** used to organize supporting ideas or details related to a topic

   Example: describing school

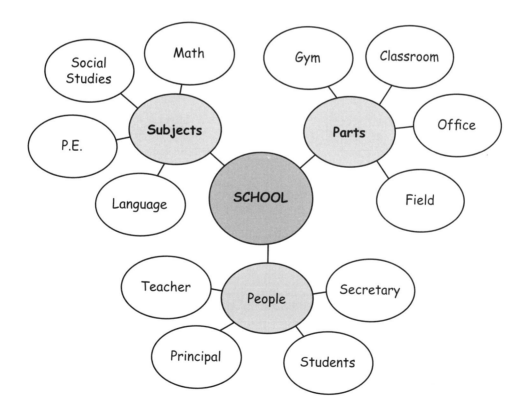

7. **Make a Picture:** used to show placement and directions

Example: from the park to the movie theater

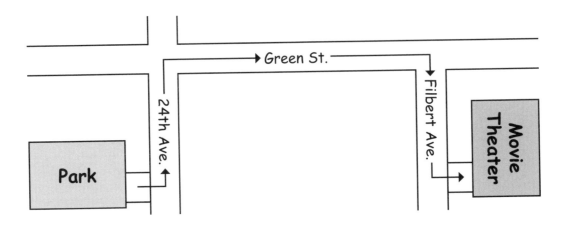

8. **Story Window:** used to show the main components of a story
(characters, setting, conflict, plot, and solution)

Example: *The Three Little Pigs*

STORY WINDOW FOR *THE THREE LITTLE PIGS*

CHARACTERS/WHO	SETTING/WHERE & WHEN
• three pigs • wolf	• straw house, stick house and brick house • fantasy (takes place during the day, but location is not specified)
CONFLICT & PROBLEM/WHY • Wolf is hungry and wants to eat pigs, but pigs do not want to be eaten SOLUTION • Pigs outwit Wolf and build a strong, brick house that the Wolf cannot destroy	**PLOT/WHAT** • Wolf tries to capture pigs and blows down straw house • Pigs move and build stick house but the Wolf blows down stick house as well • Pigs build strong, brick house that the Wolf cannot destroy

9. **Story Chart:** used to describe a story line

Example: elements needed to write a story

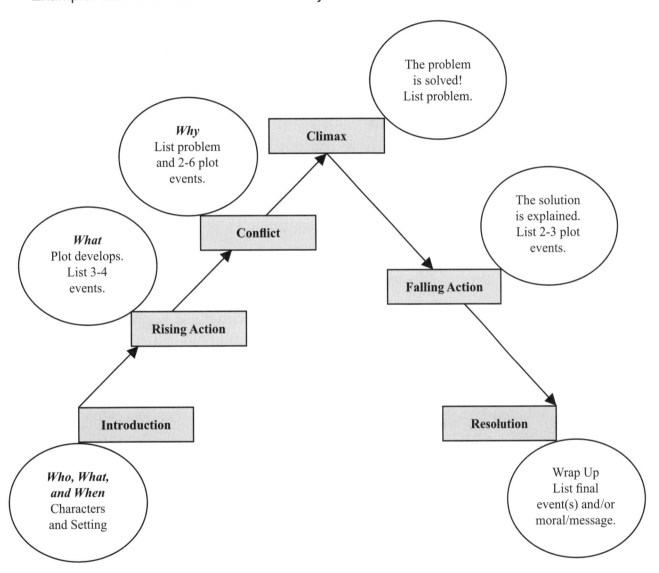

References

Becket-McWalter, J., Devine, G., Jackson, B., & Ratner, W. (2002). *Vocabulary & spelling*. NY: Learning Express.

Fotuhi, M. (2004). *The memory cure*. NY: McGraw-Hill.

Furlong, K. (1997). *Vocabulary development—Grade 3*. Grand Rapids, MI: Frank Schaffer Publications.

Higbee, K.L. (2001). *Your memory: How it works & how to improve it*. NY: Marlowe & Co.

Hobbs, J.A., & Fisher, C.D. (1994). *Summer bridge activities—Grades 4-5*. Thomasville, NC: Rainbow Bridge, a division of Carson-Dellosa, The Teacher's Tools.

Ketchum, P.J. (2001). *Spelling skills & drills—Grade 3*. Pittsburgh, PA: Hayes School Publishing Co., Inc.

Ketchum, P.J. (2001). *Spelling skills & drills—Grade 4*. Pittsburgh, PA: Hayes School Publishing Co., Inc.

Lanter, E. (2005). Language-based learning disabilities: Intrinsic and extrinsic causes. *Advance for Speech-Language Pathologists and Audiologists, 15* (43), 24.

Levine, M. (2002). *A mind at a time*. NY: Simon & Schuster.

Rothstein, V., & Termansen, R. (1997). *100% Vocabulary: Intermediate*. East Moline, IL: LinguiSystems, Inc.

Schacter, D. (1996). *Searching for memory: The brain, the mind, and the past*. NY: Basic Books.

Silbey, R. (1997). *Vocabulary development—Grade 1*. Grand Rapids, MI: Frank Schaffer Publications.

Silbey, R. (1997). *Vocabulary development—Grade 2*. Grand Rapids, MI: Frank Schaffer Publications.

Staff of Research & Education Association. (2000). *Verbal builder: An excellent review for standardized tests*. Piscataway, NJ: Research & Education Association.

Answer Key

Suggested answers listed below. Accept other logical/appropriate answers as correct.

▶ Auditory Memory

Pages 11-12
Strategies students could use to answer questions.
- 1-5: Rehearsing & Subvocalizing, Chunking
- 6-10: Rehearsing & Subvocalizing, Chunking, Linking & Associations
- 11-12: Visualizing, Paraphrasing, Identifying Key Concepts
- 13. Creating Checklists & Taking Notes, Identifying Key Concepts, Visualizing, Paraphrasing, Rehearsing & Subvocalizing, Chunking
- 14-18: Visualizing, Paraphrasing, Identifying Key Concepts
- 19. Visualizing, Paraphrasing, Identifying Key Concepts, Creating Checklists & Taking Notes, Graphing & Charting
- 20. Visualizing, Paraphrasing, Identifying Key Concepts

Pages 15-46
Answers will vary.

Pages 48-57
Exercise 1
1. Venn diagram
2. web diagram
3. bar graph or pie chart

Exercise 2
1. Venn diagram
2. bar graph
3. web diagram

Exercise 3
1. pie chart
2. Venn diagram
3. outline or web diagram

Exercise 4
1. web diagram
2. outline
3. bar graph

Exercise 5
1. outline
2. pie chart or bar graph
3. web diagram

Exercise 6
1. make a picture (order: Mandy, Sadie, Jordan, Amanda, Natasha)
2. bar graph or pie chart
3. line graph

Exercise 7
1. pie chart; Extra Credit: A+ 0, A 9, A- 1, B+ 5, B 10, B- 4, C+ 11, C 5, C- 0, D 5
2. make a picture
3. Venn diagram

Exercise 8
1. story window
2. Venn diagram
3. outline

Exercise 9
1. Venn diagram
2. story window or story chart
3. outline

Exercise 10
1. outline
2. make a picture or outline
3. make a picture

Pages 70-90
Answers will vary.

Pages 92-101
Words: Answers listed below.
Following Directions & Paragraphs: Answers will vary.

Exercise 1
1. glad
2. unhappy
3. unclear
4. street, avenue
5. below

Exercise 2
1. silly, humorous
2. stroll
3. close
4. wide
5. skinny, narrow

Exercise 3
1. seat
2. couch
3. beautiful
4. icky, gross
5. glass

Exercise 4
1. aide
2. bug
3. messy
4. instructor
5. delicious

Exercise 5
1. slice
2. helpful, nice
3. suggest, propose
4. nap, snooze
5. present

Exercise 6
1. injure
2. fall
3. carpet
4. home
5. dad

Exercise 7
1. grasp, secure
2. nap
3. finish, whole
4. breakable
5. simple

Exercise 8
1. yell
2. bawl, sob
3. shake
4. slippery
5. moist

Exercise 9
1. meeting, get-together
2. find
3. smile
4. difficult
5. branch

Exercise 10
1. show
2. ruin
3. tear
4. make
5. disappear

▶ Visual Memory

Pages 103-104
Strategies students could use to answer questions.
1. Chunking, Acronyms & Silly Sentences
2. Graphing & Charting, Identifying Key Concepts, Paraphrasing
3. Graphing & Charting, Identifying Key Concepts
4. Identifying Key Concepts, Paraphrasing, Visualizing
5. Defining & Drawing

Pages 107-116
Answers will vary.

Pages 118-127
Exercise 1
DEAR
CARE

Exercise 2
Several Dogs Bathed Happily Sitting Down Gracefully
Ask About Izzy's Pet Snake or AAIPS (apes)

Exercise 3
COPS
Dead Mice Smell Bad

Exercise 4
SCUBA
I3DCT

Exercise 5
Clouds Never See Clearly
My Very Excellent Mother Just Served Us Nachos

Exercise 6
ROY G BIV
FROM PAW

Exercise 7
HOMES
TAWWL

Exercise 8
NASA Astronauts Eat
    Apples And Avocados
WAJMMA

Exercise 9
WIPAL
All Big Boys Can Create
    Equal Fractions/Girls
    Prefer Picking Some
    Unusual Valentines

Exercise 10
Vic's Map Needed More
    Colors/Rick's Drawing
    Needed Seven New
    Numbers Painted Green
Anyone Above Five Gets
    Lunch/Maybe Nick Smith
    Takes Ten Vitamins

Pages 129-138
Answers will vary.

Pages 140-149
1. Venn diagram
2. bar graph or line graph
3. story window
4. bar graph or line graph
5. bar graph or line graph
6. pie chart
7. outline or web diagram
8. outline or web diagram
9. story window or story chart
10. outline

Pages 151-160
Exercise 1
1. Tara; Mr. Watt;
    Rashi and Shawn
2. Mrs. Cross; Brooke

Exercise 2
1. flat tire; mowed the lawn
2. play; string or ribbon;
    take a nap

Exercise 3
1. right after school; 7 p.m.
2. the week of the test;
    the morning of the test;
    the week of the test

Exercise 4
1. England; Hogwarts School
2. on a beach; in an old shoe

Exercise 5
1. They both like sports,
    hanging out with friends,
    and doing art projects.
    She is a swimmer.
2. to welcome the new year;
    a symbol of a wish for a
    sweet new year

Exercise 6
1. from the Pacific Ocean
    into the San Francisco
    Bay; the city, Alcatraz
    Island, the Bay Bridge
    and more
2. volunteer at a shelter for
    people who are homeless;
    to give back to the
    community

Exercise 7
1. Native Americans;
    their own church
2. Mr. Alt; organization
    and planning

Exercise 8
1. bassinet, car seat,
    swing, stroller or with
    their parents; sleep
2. holidays or Thanksgiving;
    a lot of people traveling
    to see their families

Exercise 9
1. at school; president;
    She lost the election;
    He won the election.
2. Orlando, Florida;
    four huge theme parks
    and two water parks;
    to take a tour of the park

Exercise 10
1. student drivers;
    pay attention to the road,
    don't talk on the phone,
    don't fiddle with the radio;
    for your safety and the
    safety of others
2. guidance counselors;
    standardized test scores;
    at the end of eighth grade;
    at schools throughout the
    country; so they choose
    classes that will meet the
    college requirements

Pages 162-171
Answers will vary.

Pages 173-182
Words: Answers listed below.
Following Directions &
Paragraphs: Answers
will vary.

Exercise 1
1. assist, aid
2. harm, injure

Exercise 2
1. wicked, criminal
2. vanish, go

Exercise 3
1. admire
2. snug, taut, strong

Exercise 4
1. chat, blather
2. ecstatic, thrilled

Exercise 5
1. strong, severe
2. shocked, disgusted

Exercise 6
1. question, inquire
2. reject, decline

Exercise 7
1. arrogant, egocentric
2. crafty, clever

Exercise 8
1. common, mainstream
    or broad, vague
2. belief, faith, hope

Exercise 9
1. removed, dislocated,
    displaced
2. moment, immediate

Exercise 10
1. intense, excessive,
    tremendous
2. inundated, besieged,
    plagued